COOKIE CUTTERS
AND MOLDS

A study of cookie cutters, Turk's Head Molds,
Butter Molds, and Ice Cream Molds

by

ARLENE AND PAUL H. GREASER

*Best Wishes
Arlene S. Greaser*

Library of Congress Card Number 70-98944

COPYRIGHT 1969—ARLENE AND PAUL H. GREASER
2638 TILGHMAN STREET
ALLENTOWN, PA. 18104

Printed by National Advertising Manufacturing Co. Inc., Allentown, Pa.

Cookie tree with three shelves and top. A mahogany English Candle Stand, circa 1750, was used to make this permanent cookie display. The colors of the candles are varied as the cookies are changed and any type ornament may be added if desired. Inspired by the Christmas pyramid, the Italian predecessor of the Yule tree in the Annie S. Kemerer Museum, Bethlehem, Penna. and the Zoe Kauffman tree, referred to in the Lancaster New Era, Lancaster, Penna. December 20, 1965.

Dedicated to

EILEEN PATRICIA HOOK
and to
MICHAEL CHARLES HOOK

with appreciation to

A. A. Auld, Esq.
Ray R. Brennen, Esq.
Fritz Hahn
Florence John
Arnold R. Mountford, F.M.A.
Viola L. Neiman
Hedwig Overcht
Roger W. Pease, Jr.
Mr. and Mrs. Carl Snavely
Elaine Timbers

Cookie Cutters

(O)NLY recently has the cookie cutter been acknowledged and recognized as an outstanding example of Pennsylvania Dutch folk art and as a result of this and its contribution to all folk art they are now considerably in demand by museums, historical societies, and private collectors.

It has been said that rural art is by no means an undeveloped or discarded bourgeois art, but rather a branch of art in general and that ancient traditions and even prehistoric influences can be traced in it; not to a superior civilization does it owe form or technique, but far oftener are these an ancient heritage faithfully preserved.

In "Touch of the Dutchland"—Dr. Earl F. Robacker tells us that nowhere is there to be found, in the decorative arts of Pennsylvania, such a wealth and rich variety of design, such a range of imagination, and such a correlation between history and art and he asks how such a fruitful source of information could have for so long gone unnoticed by the student and many are the requests that we have recently had for a pictorial display of a goodly number in a convenient manner to enable further study of this humble medium of expression.

They are used especially at the Christmas holidays and we will list for the student some of the facts we have found for his guidance and some of the tremendous number of examples available in such a large and fertile field.

Christmas is the principal holiday of the year among the Pennsylvania Dutch and Frederick Klees in—The Pennsylvania Dutch—The MacMillan Company—1950 tells us that the Christmas trees were hung with conventional glass balls, that apples and cookies were hung on many of the trees until the latter years of the last century, and especially animal cookies decorated with red sugar. He recalls to our memory the custom of the children making long strings of popcorn and cranberries to decorate the tree, chains of brightly colored paper rings, nuts covered with tinfoil, icicles of tinfoil or glass, shepherd's crooks of red and white peppermint candy, little baskets and even pretzel shaped candy of the same peppermint type hard candy, with, of course, the conventional "Star of Bethlehem" for the top of the tree.

In the December 22, 1968 issue of "TODAY" supplement of the "PHILADELPHIA INQUIRER" Frances Spatz Leighton gave an excellent description of the 20 foot fir tree installed in the White House by Mrs. Johnson, how with research through the experts at the Smithsonian Institution she learned how our forefathers decorated their trees and how she accordingly applied fresh or dried fruit and nuts, nosegays, all kinds of small toys, and Gingerbread cookies of every Christmassy shape and decoration such as teddy bears, horses, snowmen, milkmaids, Santa Clauses, Christmas trees, and stars.

The Putz is a creche, a decorative portrayal, by means of molded figures, of the Nativity, a custom which could possibly have been brought over to this country from the area of Provence, in the south of France.

Some of these displays are rather elaborate and Mr. Klees describes the custom of putzing in the Moravian settlements, or of going from house to house to see the displays of those who have, or who have boasted of having more elaborate displays. Because of the growth of the custom and the number of guests the hosts are no longer able, unless to their best or most intimate friends, to serve, as they once did, the traditional wine and cookies, marzipan hearts, or brown and white Moravian cookies.

Since hospitality, trees with their appeal to children and food seem to be some of the visible evidences of the "Spirit of Christmas" we felt an interest in learning if this was a universal custom and learned some interesting thoughts and customs a further study of which we recommend to those who find research interesting since we do not have the space to cover them fully, nor would it serve the purpose we have in mind, but, we will name a few which seem pertinent, or especially interesting.

In Spain we believe that the children just pretend to be asleep on the night of January 5, for their hearts are pounding with excitement and anticipation of what is arriving through the skies to be placed in their shoes. The Three Kings, The Wise Men, come, they believe, on camel across burning deserts, on horse through snow-covered mountain ranges, and they hop neatly on their own power up to windows with their loads.

Cities and most villages organize public cavalcades, with fireworks, a sumptuous spectacle, for the triumphal entry of the Three Kings, to cheers of the children who are completely enchanted by the splendor. All of the children are committed to this belief in the Three Kings and the parents must, of necessity, make the dreams come true. The emphasis in Spain on Christmas is on peace, quiet and the joys of family life, which is recalled in homes by the crib installed there.

During the holiday season they do have a day of feasting, we understand, but this is on January 1—(New Years Eve). This is celebrated with groaning tables laden with all manner of delicious dishes and gathered around are grandparents, grandchildren—the food varies from baked sea-bream to eel-fry, almond soup, turkey, lamb and delicious turren, together with sherries and champagne. The twelve strokes of the bell welcome the New Year and in Madrid's traditional Puerta del Sol people pack together and gobble down the twelve grapes to be consumed before the strokes cease. After this come drinking toasts to the New Year with champagne, shouts of gaiety and rejoicing.

In Sweden, while Christmas occurs on December 25, the holiday seems to creep along its magic way through much of December due to its ancient tradition and folklore and everything seems to have a special meaning.

In "Once upon a Christmas Time" by Thyra Ferre' Bjorn-Holt, Rinehart and Winston—1964 we learn that "Tomte" was a cross between an Irish leprechaun and Holland's St. Nicholas and she describes in a very interesting manner the "Crown of St. Lucia" and the Festival of Lights.

Following the Festival of Lights on December 13, it seems, their thoughts turn immediately to the preparations for the fast approaching holidays and all of the visiting and entertaining that accompanies it. One of the first of these was the baking of hundreds and hundreds of cookies in as many as 29 different kinds. Each cookie was a unique creation and they were placed in tightly covered tins and stored in the cold earth cellar, not to be opened until the afternoon before Christmas.

They include Christmas Angels and Stars in honor of Bethlehem, Santa Clauses, Christmas logs and half-moons, Oak leaves and rings, S-shaped cookies and braided wreaths and many, many more, as well as Bucks and Santa's large enough to hang on the Christmas tree.

The tree plundering was an invitation affair and started about January 2nd and on successive days thereafter so that most of the children could attend several of these parties. After songs and games the children would prance around the tree, picking it clean and placing their trophies in a big heap on the long table already holding a paper bag and an apple for each child expected. The goodies were divided equally, cookies and cake were added to each childs pile and punch was served the children who were this day honored guests.

In "Christmastide" Its History, Festivities, and Carols" by William Sandys, F.S.A.—John Russell Smith, London—1833 we find references to this season appearing as early as in the twelfth century, and among the customs which may interest the reader was the custom regarding the use of mistletoe. It indicated that if one can, by favour or cunning, induce a fair one to come under the mistletoe he is entitled to a salute, and at the same time he should wish her a happy new year, and present to her one of the berries for good luck; each bough, therefore, is laden, he says, with a limited number of kisses, which should be well considered in selecting one.

It is not recorded if each individual has his own mistletoe branch or if it was a family branch to be shared by all but we are told that the Druids celebrated a grand festival on the annual cutting of the mistletoe, which was held on the sixth day of the moon nearest their new year and that they were in the habit of dispensing the plant at a high price.

Mr. Sandys continues however to tell us that while the well-known minced or Christmas pie is of considerable antiquity and hundreds of them appear at the lord-mayor's feast on the 9th of November he feels that they should be confined to the season of Christmas and that the north of England is celebrated for its Christmas pies of a different description, composed of turkeys, geese, game, and various small birds, weighing sometimes half a hundred weight and upwards, and calculated to meet the attacks of a large Christmas party throughout the festival. Plum-pudding, of which the old name is said to have been "hackin" until the time of Charles the Second, is another valuable dish.

There was a time, he adds, when there was much hospitality and an English gentleman, at the opening of the great day, had all his tenants and neighbors enter his hall by day-break and he proceeds to describe the strong beer, the Black-jacks, which went plentifully about with toast, sugar, nutmeg, and good Cheshire cheese; the time when they ate sirloins of roast beef for breakfast, etc.

He quotes from Gervase Markham's account in his "English House-wife" of a moderate dinner of this time and its prevalent profusion—The first course should consist of sixteen full dishes; that is, dishes of meat that are of substance, and not empty, or for show—as thus, for example; first, a shield of brawn, with mustard; secondly, a boyl'd capon; thirdly, a boyl'd piece of beef; fourthly, a chine of beef, rosted; fifthly, a neat's tongue, rosted; sixthly, a pig, rosted; seventhly, chewets, baked; eighthly, a goose, rosted; ninthly, a swan, rosted; tenthly, a turkey, rosted; eleventhly, a haunch of venison, rosted; the twelfth, a pasty of venison; thirteenth, a kid, with a pudding in the belly; the fourteenth, an olive-pye; the fifteenth, a couple of capons; the sixteenth, a custard, or dowsets. Now, to these full dishes may be added, sallets, fricases, quelque cheses, and devised paste, as many dishes more, which make the full service no less than two and thirty dishes; which is as much as can conveniently stand on one table, and in one mess. And after this manner you may proportion both your second and third courses, holding fulness on one half of the dishes, and show in the other; which will be both frugal in the splendour, contentment to the guest, and much pleasure and delight to the beholder.

Shortly before his book was written he says that the Christmas tree was introduced from the continent and it is of much amusement to old and young, and much taste can be displayed and expense incurred in preparing its glittering and attractive *fruit*. It is, he says, delightful to watch the animated expectation and enjoyment of the children as the treasures are displayed and distributed; the parents equally participating in the pleasure, and enjoying the sports of their childhood over again. And, he adds, where can the weary world-worn man find greater relief from his anxious toil and many cares, and haply his many sorrows, than in contemplating the amuse-ments of artless children, and discover the right "Simon Pure".

Washington Irving in "Old Christmas and Bracebridge Hall, Mac-Millan and Co.—London—1886 points out that while the traditional cus-toms of golden-hearted antiquity with its feudal hospitalities, and lordly wassalings have passed away with the baronial castles and stately manor-houses Christmas is still a period of delightful excitement in England. It is, he tells us, gratifying to see that home feeling completely aroused which seems to hold so powerfully a place in every English bosom. The prepara-tions making on every side for the social board that is again to unite friends and kindred; the presents of good cheer passing and repassing, those tokens of regard, and quickeners of kind feelings; the evergreens distributed about houses and churches, emblems of peace and gladness; all these have the most pleasing effect in producing fond associations, and kindling benevo-lent sympathies.

Miles & John Hadfield in "The Twelve Days of Christmas"—Cassell & Company Ltd.—London—1961 tell us that cakes and pastries, gingerbreads, and other forms of confectionery are international and that many are associated with a particular country or locality such as Nuremberg for its Lebkuchen or spice cakes and Lubeck and Konigsberg for their marzipan, a paste of almonds and sugar moulded into ornamental shapes and which is, in Britain, known as marchpane.

They advise that gingerbreads go back to the fifteenth century, that they were made in a variety of forms such as man, animals, letters of the alphabet, etc. and that shapes made for the season were made also in the image of Christmastide characters.

In "Christmas—Its Carols, Customs and Legends" by Ruth Heller—Schmitt, Hall & McCreary Company—Minneapolis—1948 we learn that in ancient Rome cakes in the form of animals and people were presented as gifts to the senators. They became more and more elaborate and were eventually adopted for use at Christmas time. In old England it was the custom to give cakes to poor women who sang in the streets during Christmastide.

If, in fact, gingerbreads go back to the fifteenth century and if they were in the forms of man, animals, letters of the alphabet it would seem that there must have been cutters, molds, or some means of securing a uniformity and ease of producing them at that time. If they were presented to the senators in ancient Rome, it would seem that the same must apply.

We understand that "Handbook of Tomorrows Antiques" by Charles Drepperd and Marjorie Smith gives credit to the Pennsylvania Dutch for introducing wooden molds in the seventeenth century, carved, so as to produce springerle, marzipan and Christmas cakes, circular, to be hung on the Christmas tree and to be eaten before Twelfthnight. The subjects were religious, historic, royal, commemorative, animal and military. In fact in his "A Dictionary of American Antiques" Carl W. Drepperd—Charles T. Branford Company—Boston—1952 tells us that molds (for marchpane) as early as the 16th century are known and that he has in his collection a example dated 1563—many, he says, are of a ceremonial nature and quite large.

The cover page of "Antiques" December 1923 has a mould for Spice Cakes dated 1676, wooden and beautifully carved—On page 286 and 287 are additional wooden cake moulds (German), the one a young man and a young lady and the other the seal of the city of Nuremberg used they say for the fearsome type of indestructible gingerbread, known as Nurnberger Lebkuchen. There is another pictured dated also 1676 and carved to depict Saul and David.

The Diderot Encyclopedia—Recuil de Planches Sur Les Sciences, Les Arts Lineraux Et Les Arts Mechaniques, Paris, 1762-1777 has a page marked Pl.2 which contains a Turk's Head Mold and a heart shaped cutter #21 for cookies and figure #4 could, in fact, be an outline cutter of a type with which we have not yet seen, but this will indicate that in 1762 this metal cookie cutter was a known and used necessity in France.

In fact "A Diderot Pictorial Encyclopedia of Trades and Industry" by

Denis Diderot—Dover Publications Inc.—New York—1959 plate 147 Volume 1 says that plating sheet iron with tin to render it rust-proof was already an old process in the 18th century. It had been introduced into France from Bohemia and Germany by Colbert a little less than a century before the Encyclopedia was published.

In "Early American decorated Tinware" by Beatrice Farnsworth Powers and Olive Floyd—Hastings House, New York—1957 we learn that Shem Drowne was the first Tinsmith in the American Colonies, about 1720, and that the items he made are today very highly regarded but that he did not reach the large scale operation reached about 1740 by Edward Pattison in Berlin, Connecticut.

In "The Tinsmiths of Connecticut" by Shirley Spaulding Devoe— Wesleyan University Press—Middletown, Conn.—1968 the author clears up the mystery of the date of the start of the Pattison operation and his age at death.

After 1760 Edward Pattison began to teach others the trade but the revolution put a stop to the import of tin and it was not until about 1810 that it really got another start and by this time the makers had to secure larger markets, the housewives about Connecticut already having a goodly supply of each type made, and peddlers began to cover the country to dispose of this new found necessity. The journeyman tinsmith was a trained worker and a resourceful one so that his wagon was a travelling shop in which he carried his materials, his equipment, his tools and his belongings. He would set up shop in his wagon for a day, for two days or for as long a period of time as there was a demand for his services, and frequently these mechanics would remain in a town permanently. Thomas Passmore made tinware for the household in Philadelphia, we believe, from 1790 through the early 1800's.

Alice Morse Earle in "Home Life in Colonial Days"—Grosset & Dunlap—New York—1898 tells us that the colonial housewifes candied fruits and nuts, made many marmalades and quiddonies, and a vast number of fruit wines and cordials. Even their cakes, pies, and puddings, she tells us, were most complicated, and humble households were lavish in the various kinds they manufactured and ate.

While the first truly American cookbook was, we believe, published in 1796 there were prior cookbooks available and the same would apply to molds, to cutters, and to the other vessels and implements required to produce the food described.

The wooden molds were the earlier type, those with a wooden back and a tin cutting edge seem to have followed and those completely of metal and tin came last. The most accurate gauge of age would probably be the weight or gauge of the metal since the makers chose a lighter gauge metal as it became available and the heavier metals are the older but it is, of course, the subject matter, the thinking and an analysis of our heritage which prompts the collection and study of this item.

Our grandparents had a number of recipes available to please any and all tastes but the variety of the subjects they used to lend enchantment or cause comment on their efforts of cookie baking is what today intrigues us and gives a tangible item to study more closely their thoughts, their humor, their knowledge, their reactions—our heritage.

The tinsmith carried a number of patterns and these were carefully drawn and executed so that these cutters were faithfully and uniformly produced but when the housewife requested one that the tinsmith did not have a pattern for and he had to produce a reasonable facsimile or loose the sale, many of the examples indicate that he did not loose the sale— he supplied us with some examples that are difficult to identify and a vivid imagination must frequently be used.

Many cutters have markings that we are told identified the maker but to date, as far as we are aware, this has not been verified. Very few have the name of the maker and these are valued very highly and are retained by the fortunate collector who found them.

We list some of our collection to provide the student an opportunity to study them more closely.

1—Dog carved in 8¼ x 5 wooden block

1A—Intricate carving on reverse of #1

2—The Lovers—Man on horseback

2A—The Lovers—Reverse of #2—Lady

3—Lamb—6 x 5 inch wooden block

4—Pair of gloves—carved in 5½ x 3 block—This side glove for right hand, reverse identically carved glove for left hand.

12

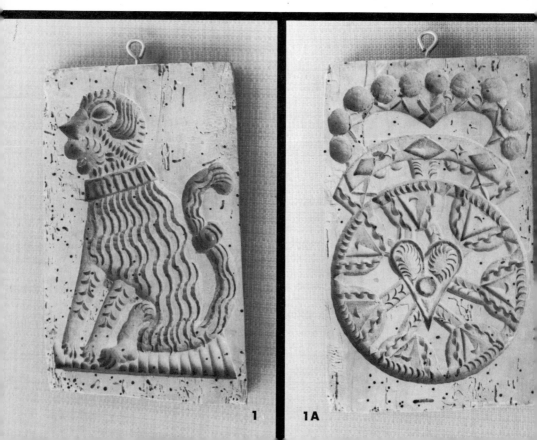

1   1A

2

2A

3

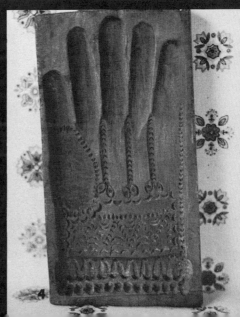

4

5—Bunch of grapes carved in 6 x 12½ wooden block with a tin cutting edge.

6—Wooden cookie cutters with a tin cutting edge.
   Under tin cookie cutters—the type we are most accustomed to seeing we will list only a few from our collection to give an idea as to the variety to be found and the type of work and the imagination of these tinsmiths, 7 to 63—animals, 64 to 68 fish, and 69 & 70 turtles.

7—We presume was intended to be an anteater

8—Appears to be an alligator

9—A boar

10—Buffalo

14

5

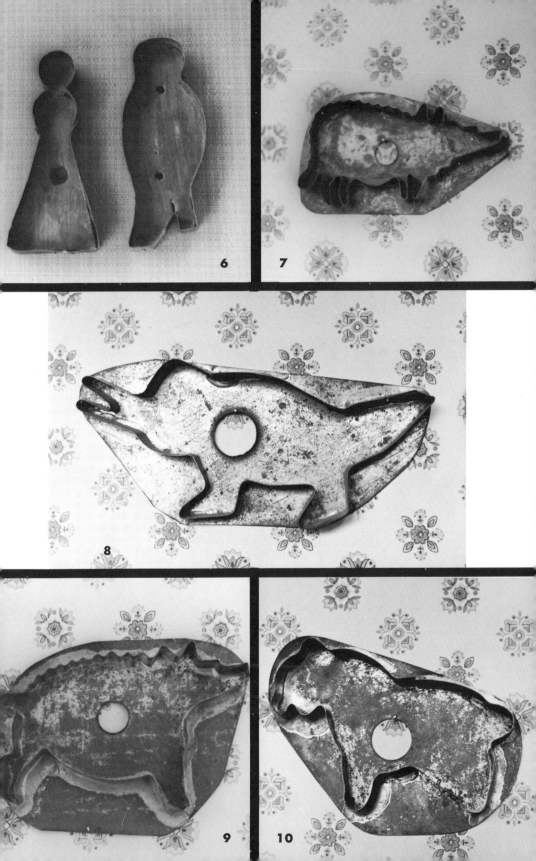

6

7

8

9   10

11—Bear

12—Bear

13—Bear

14—Teddy bear

15—Camel

16—Camel

16

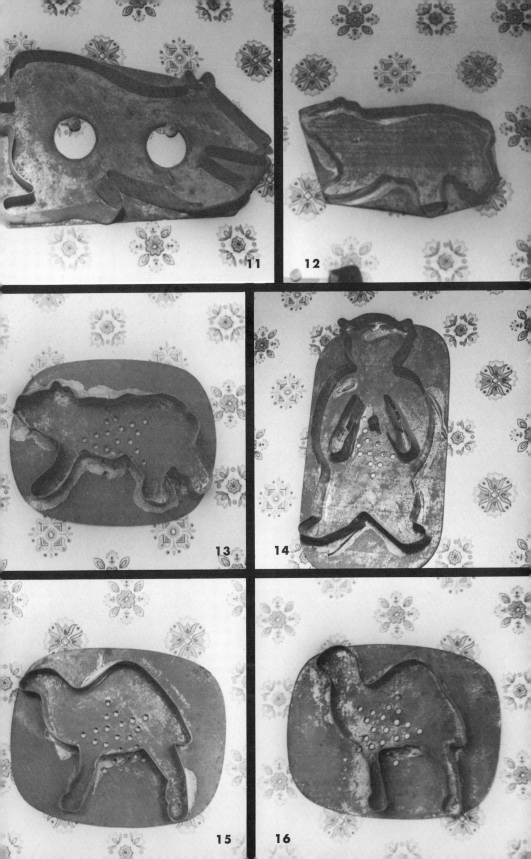

11 12

13 14

15 16

17—Cat

18—Cat

19—Chipmunk

20—Cow

21—Deer

22—Deer

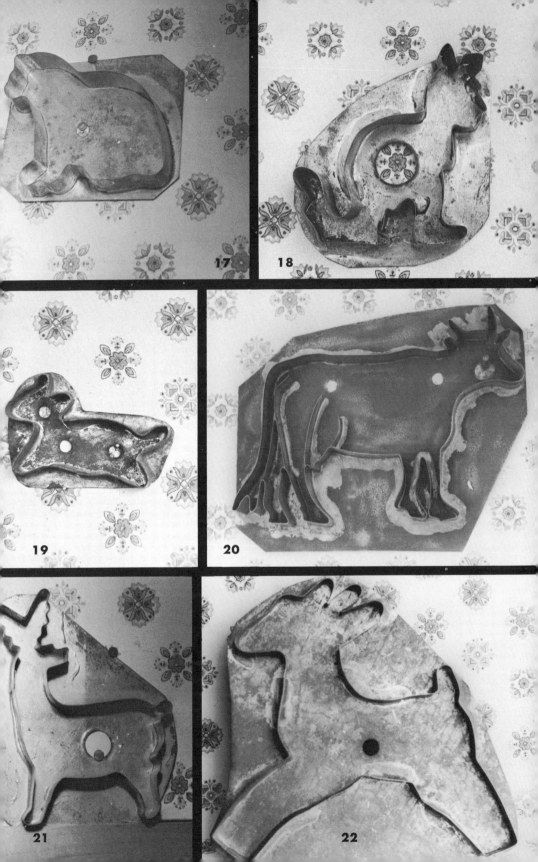

17

18

19

20

21

22

20

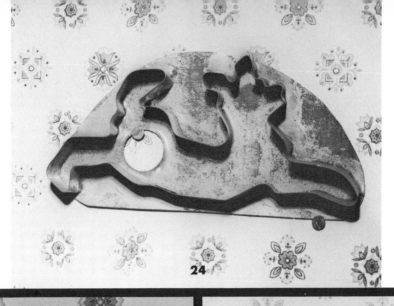

24

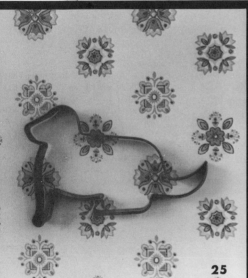

25

26

27

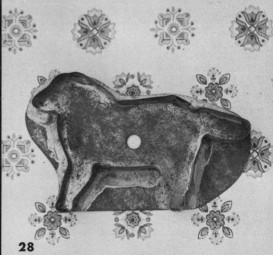

28

22

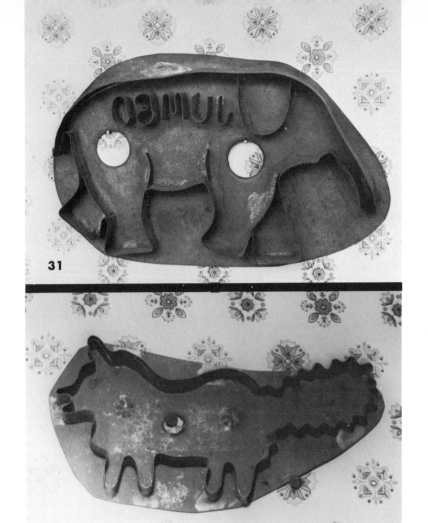

31

32

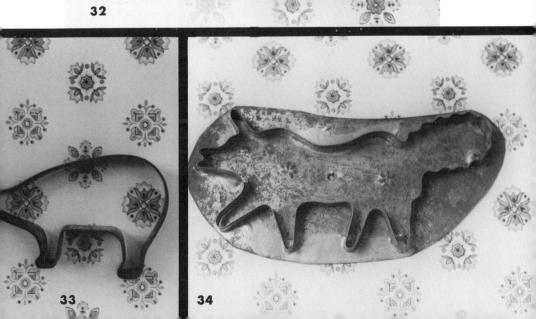

33

34

24

35

36

37

38

39

40

26

41

42

43

44

45 46

46—Lion

47—Lion

48—Moose

49—Mouse

50—Pig

51—Rabbit

46

47

48

49

50

51

52—Rabbit

53—Rabbit

54—Rabbit

55—Rabbit

56—Rabbit

57—Rabbit

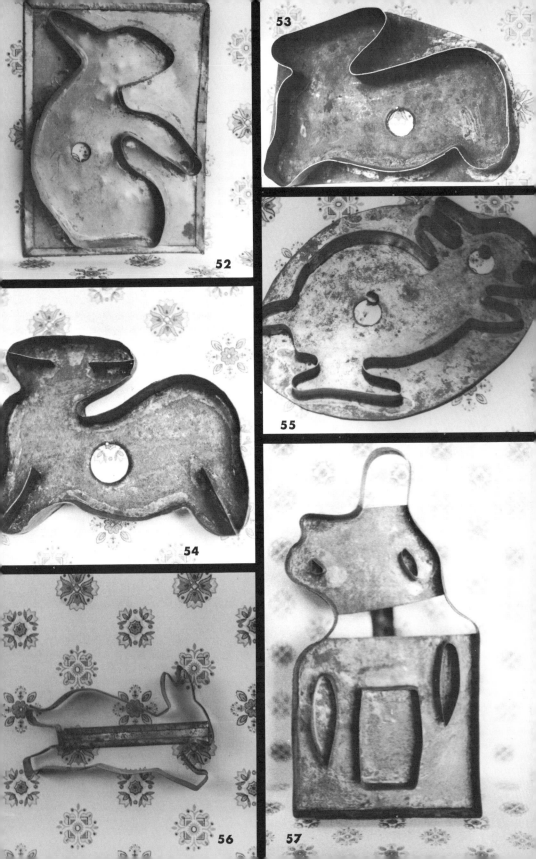

52

53

54

55

56

57

58—Rhinoceros

59—Squirrel

60—Squirrel

61—Squirrel

62—Squirrel

63—Lion rampant

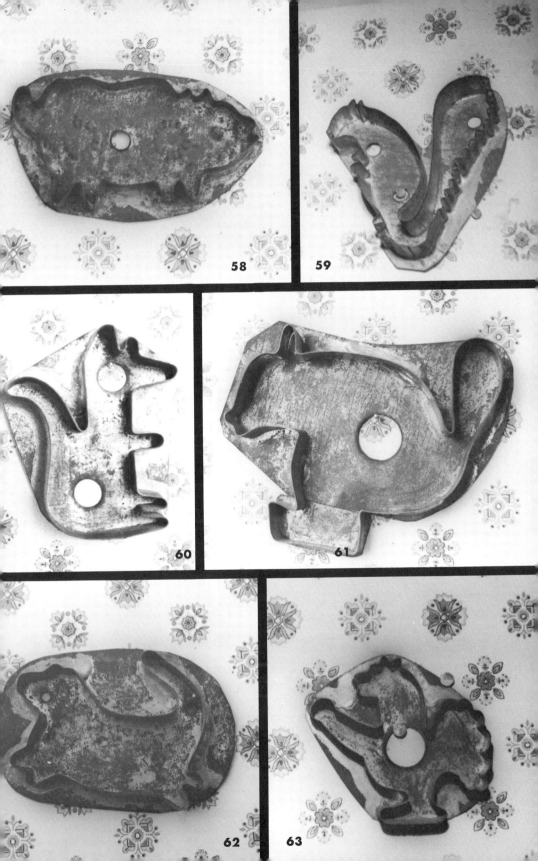

58

59

60

61

62 63

64—Fish

65—Fish

66—Fish

67—Fish

68—Fish

69—Turtle small

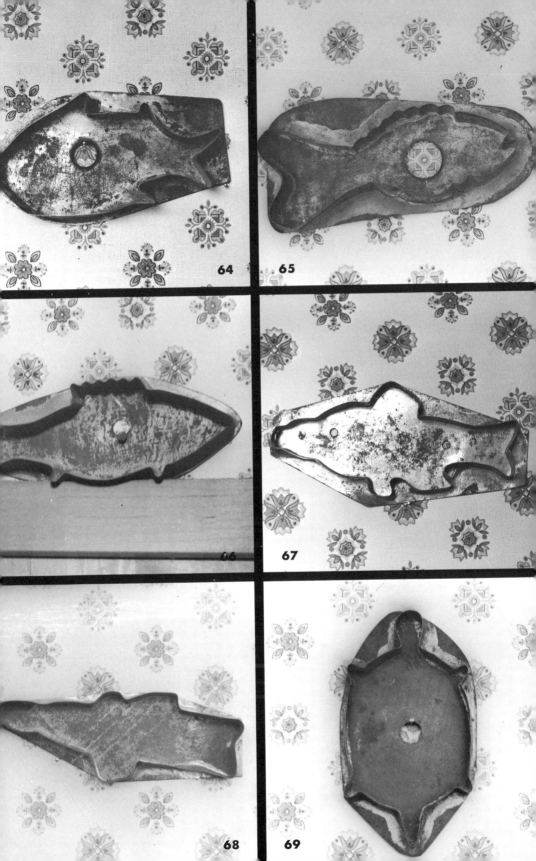

64

65

66

67

68

69

70—Turtle large

The fowl are even harder to identify and numbers 71 to 110 will give the reader some idea.

71—Bird

72—Bird with crown

73—Bird

74—Bird

75—Bird

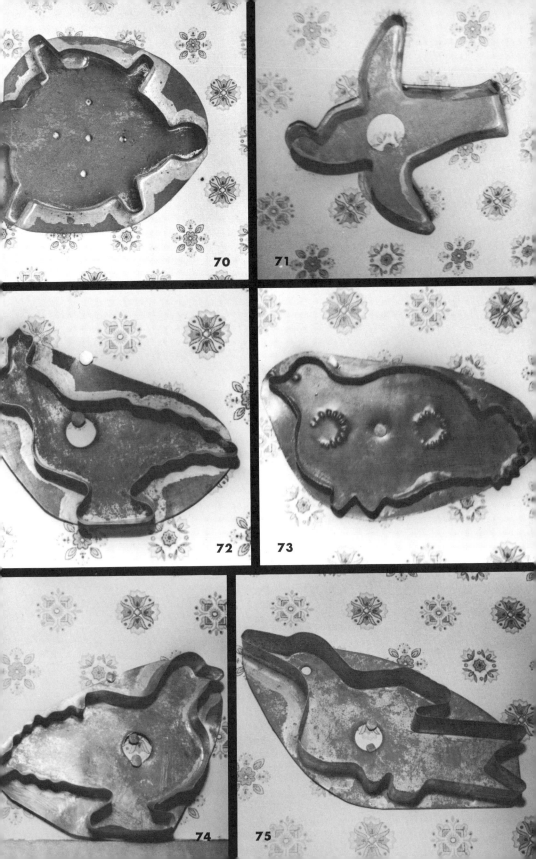

76—Bird

77—Bird

78—Bird

79—Bird

80—Bird

81—Bird

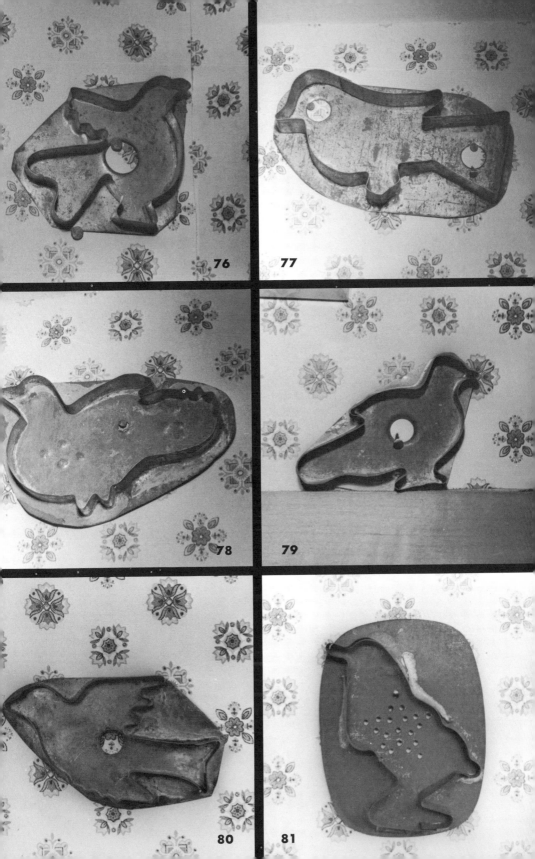

76

77

78

79

80

81

82—Bird
83—Bird
84—Eagle
85—Eagle
86—Eagle
87—Eagle

40

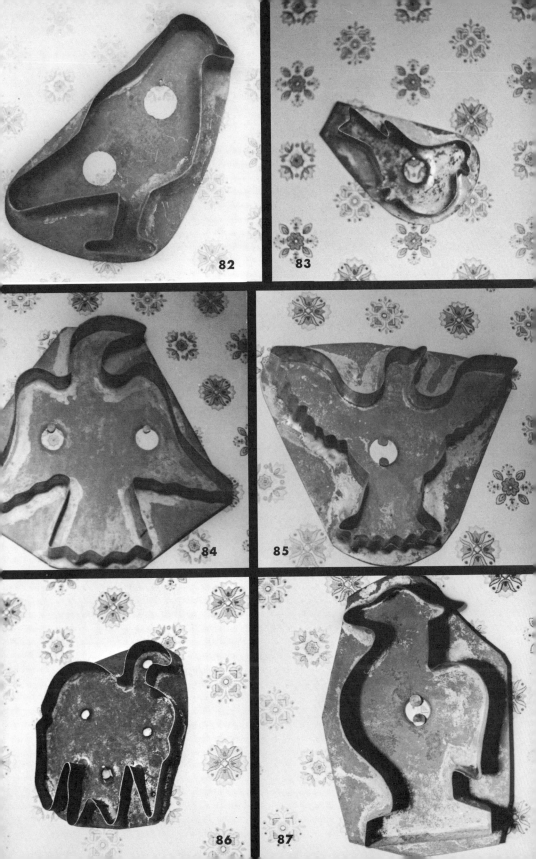

88—Duck

89—Goose

90—Goose

91—Goose

92—Goose

93—Hen

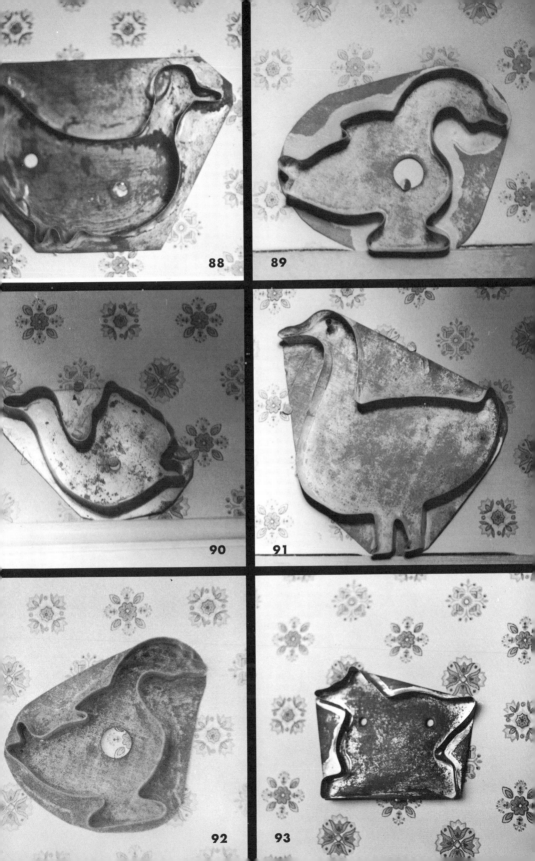

44

94

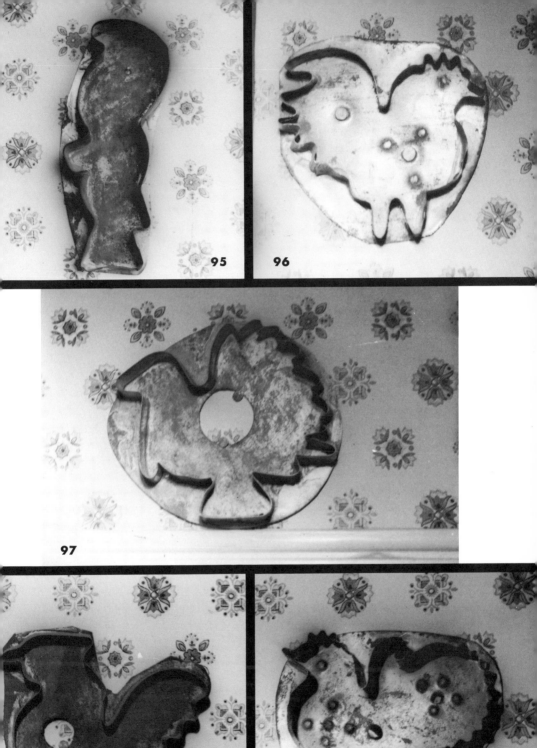

95

96

97

98

99

100—Rooster

101—Rooster

102—Rooster

103—Rooster

104—Rooster

105—Rooster

46

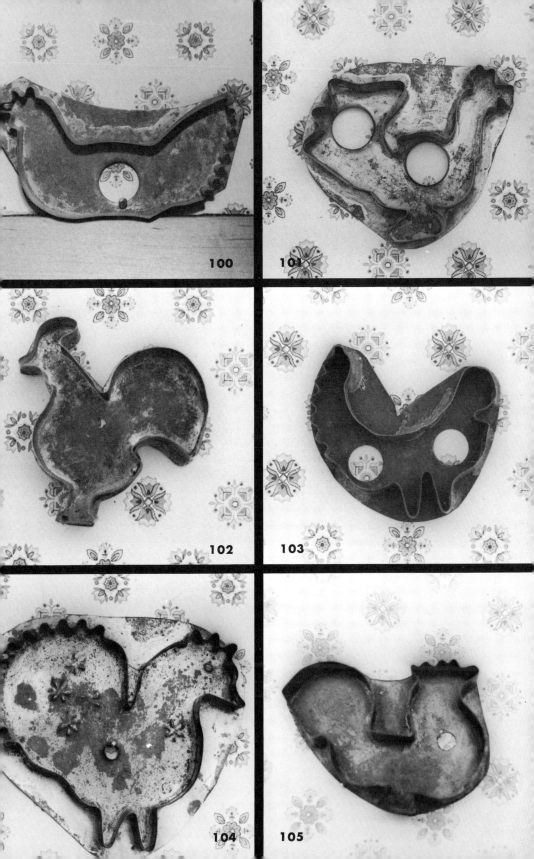

100

101

102

103

104

105

106—Rooster

107—Rooster

108—Peacock

109—Swan

110—Stork

111—Pelican

48

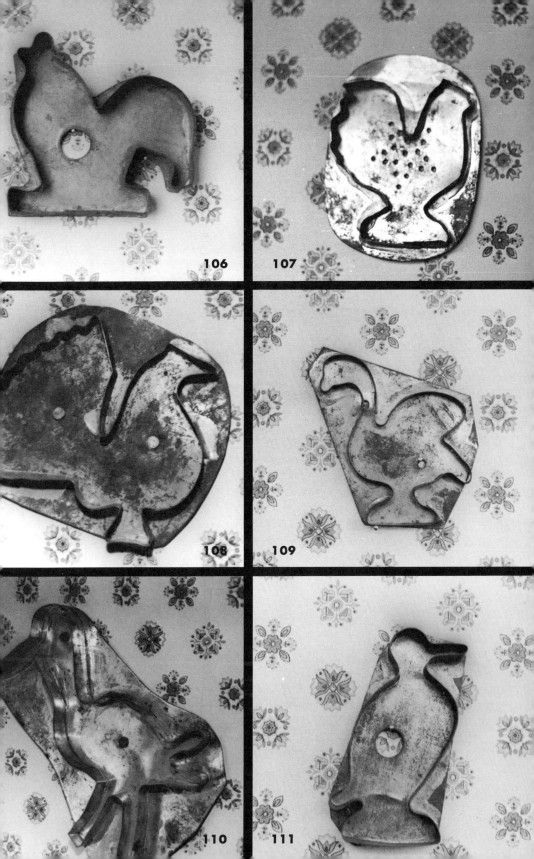

106

107

108

109

110

111

112—Pelican

Some flowers can easily be identified and some are difficult.

113—Tulip

114—Tulip

115—Tulip

116—Tulip

117—Thistle

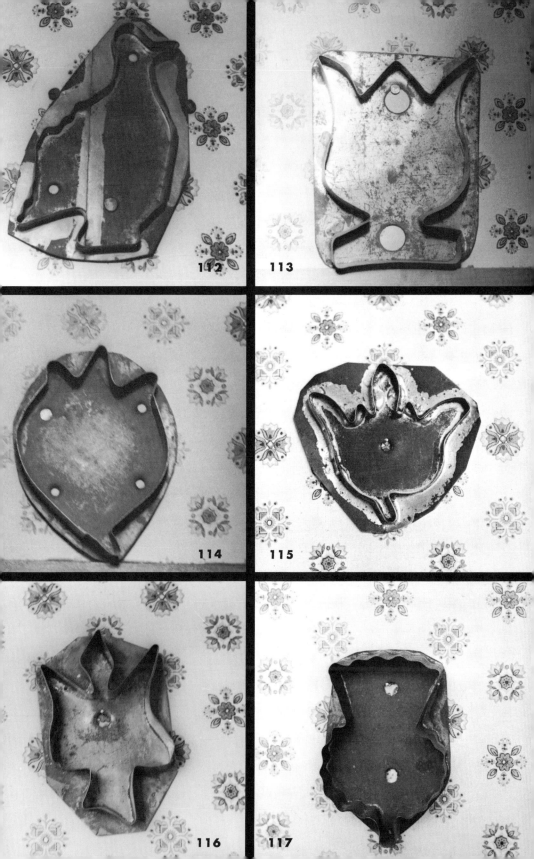

112 113

114 115

116 117

118—Unidentified

119—Unidentified

120—Unidentified

121—Unidentified

122—Unidentified

123—Unidentified

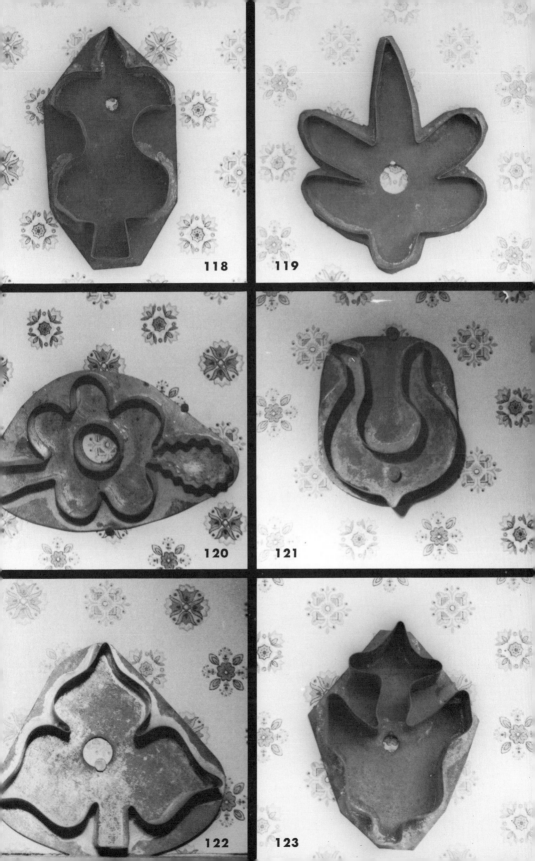

118 119

120 121

122 123

Hearts come in a variety of types.

124—Heart, normal

125—Heart, smaller

126—Heart, pinched bottom

127—Heart, elongated

128—Heart, irregular

129—Heart, serated edge

124

125

126

127

128

129

130—Heart, serated edge with insert

131—Heart with hand

People are supplied in many types as can be readily determined by the following examples.

132—Lady

133—Lady

134—Lady

135—Lady

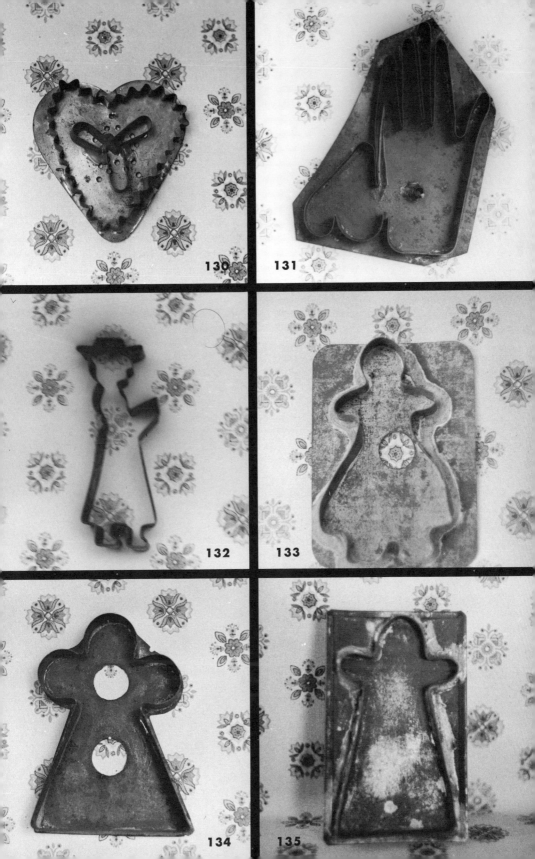

130

131

132

133

134

135

58

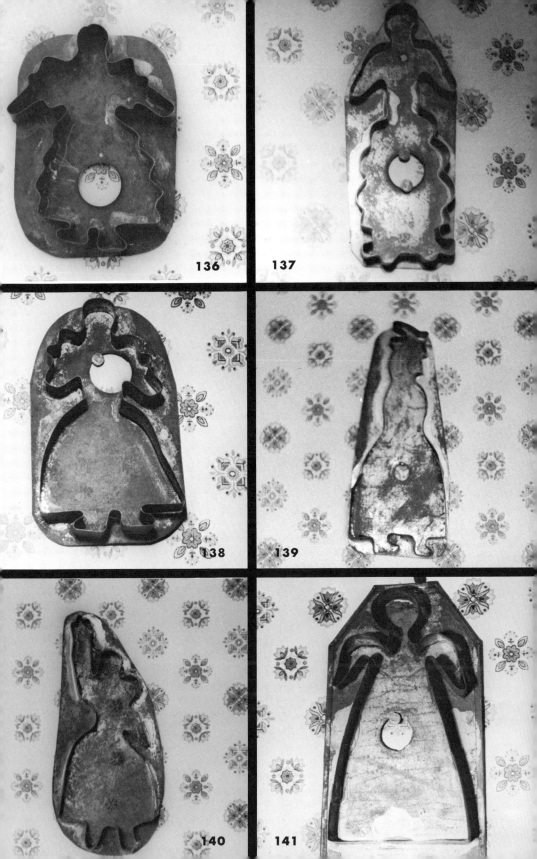

136

137

138

139

140

141

142—Twin girls

143—Man and Lady Heads only

144—Man

145—Man

146—Man

147—Man

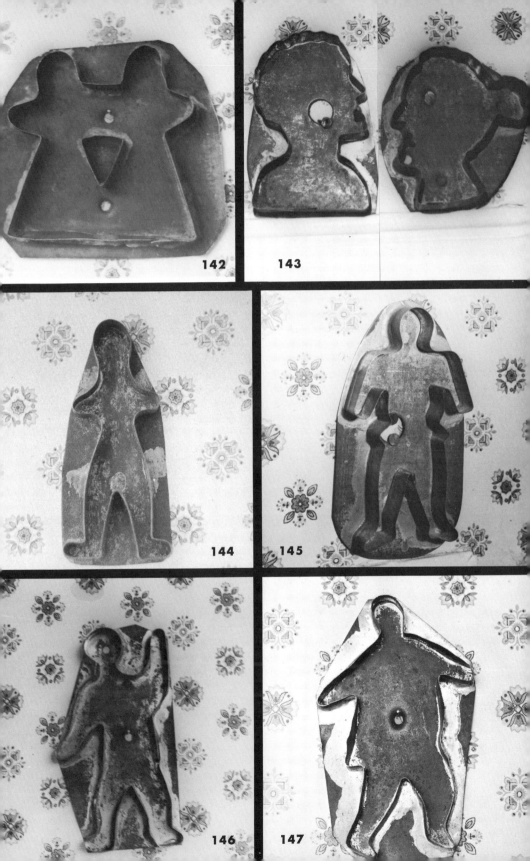

142

143

144

145

146 147

62

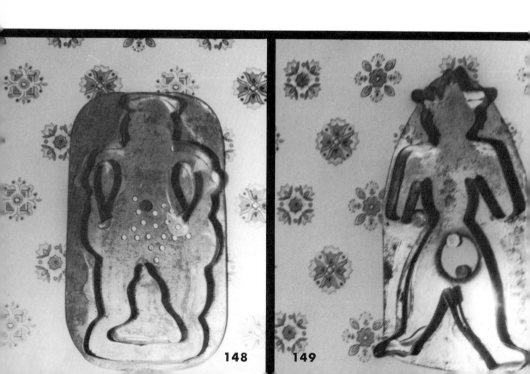

148   149

150   151

152   153

154—Indian with tomahawk

155—Indian with papoose

156—Indian with feather headdress

157—Man on horseback usually referred to as Paul Revere

Stars may still be stars but they differed in accordance with the maker and/or the desires of the purchaser.

158—5 pointed star

159—8 pointed star

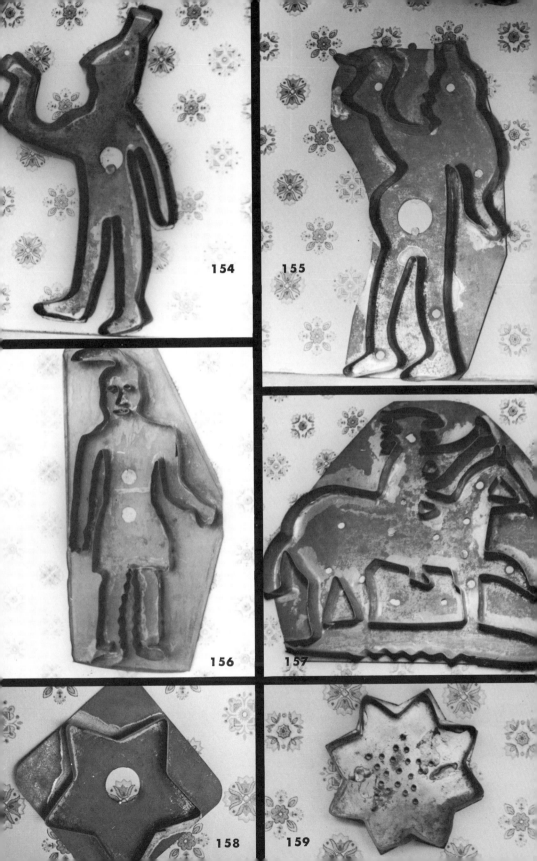

154

155

156

157

158

159

160—7 pointed star

161—8 pointed star of Lancaster Penna. manufacturer it appears since the designs on back are of the type found on a number of extremely early Lancaster area guns.

161A—Back of cutter #161.
Musical instruments must of necessity be included and a few follow.

162—Mandolin

163—Mandolin we presume

164—Unidentified

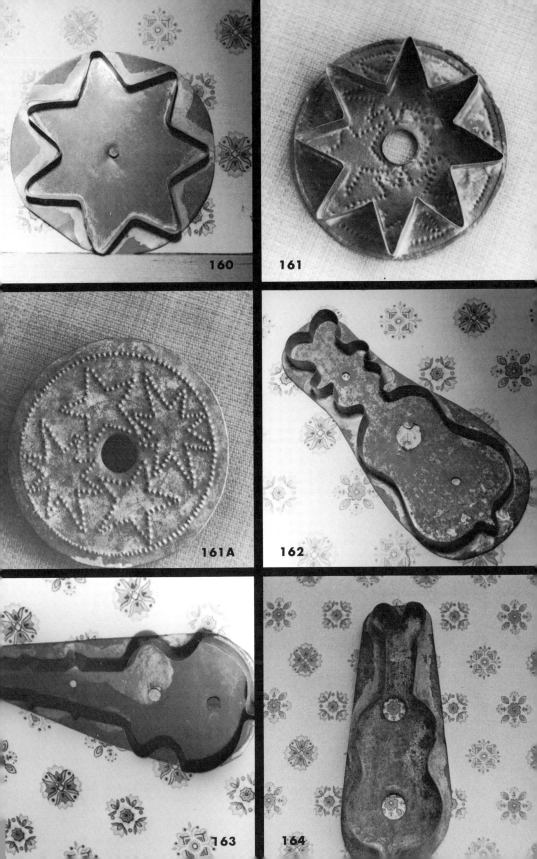

160

161

161A

162

163

164

165—Unidentified

166—Spruce tree

167—Spruce tree

168—Leaf

169—Leaf

170—Leaf

68

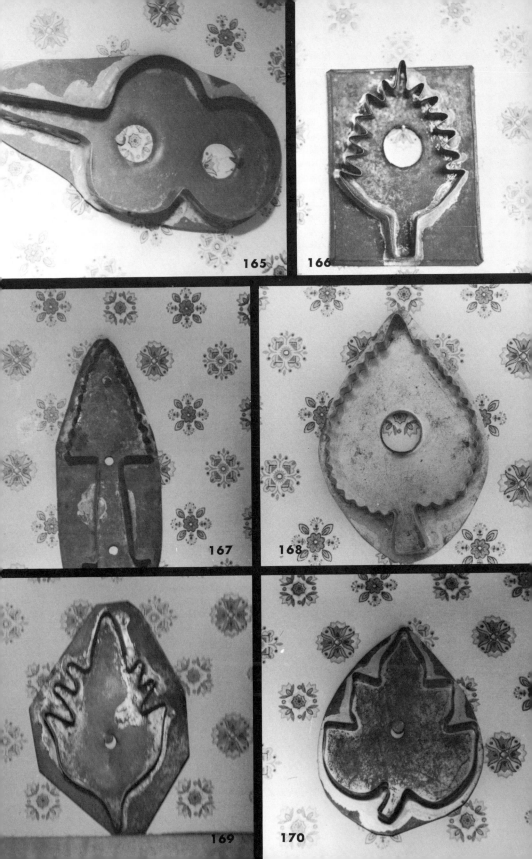

165

166

167

168

169

170

70

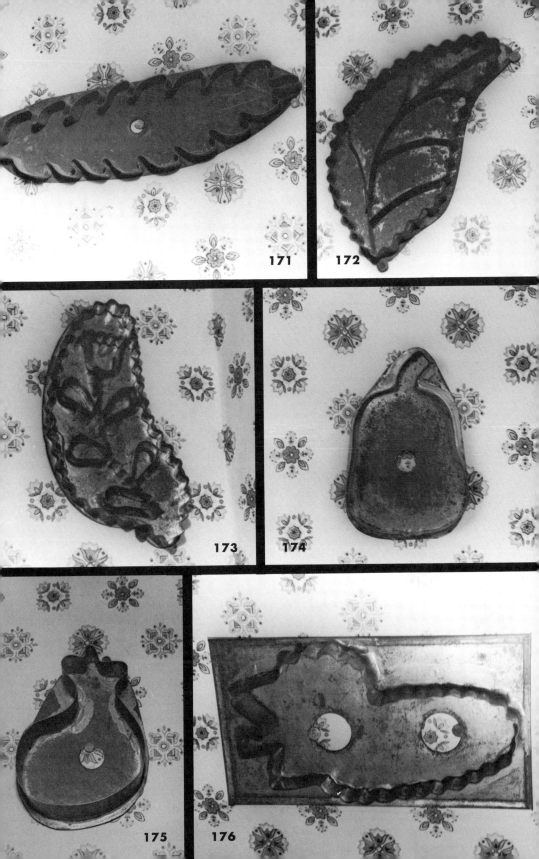

171

172

173

174

175

176

177—Unidentified but one of a large number of miscellaneous cutters which so intrigued the housewife who wanted an outstanding, a different cutter so that her handiwork could be easily identified in the quiet way they preferred.

178—Tophat

179—Shoe

180—Boot

181—Boot

182—Pitcher

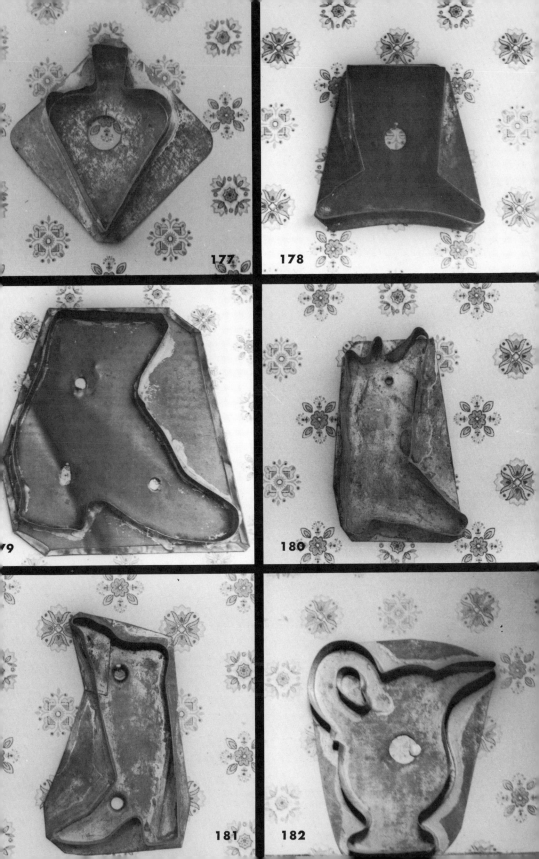

177
178
79
180
181
182

183—Sprinkling can

184—Hatchet

185—Whisk broom

186—Anchor

187—Anchor

188—Star flower

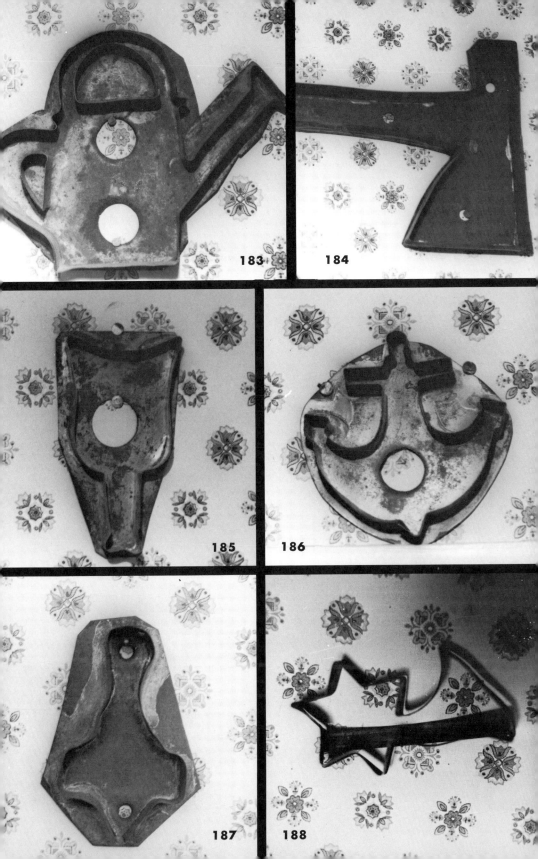

183 184 185 186 187 188

189—Shield

190—Horseshoe

191—Letter "D"

192—Pipe

193—Moon

194—Hand

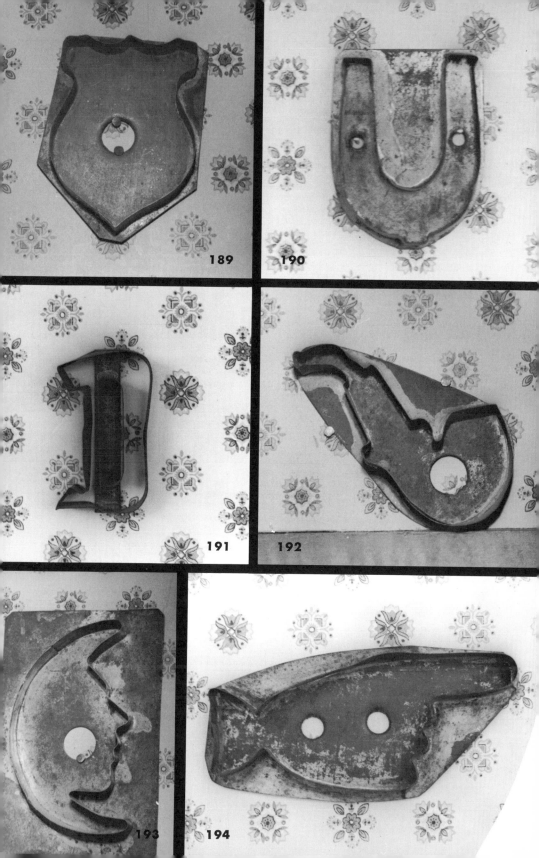

189

190

191

192

193

194

195—Hand

196—Hand

197—Teardrop

198—One plate with six cutter each teardrop shaped

199—Christmas tree ornament

200—Unidentified

78

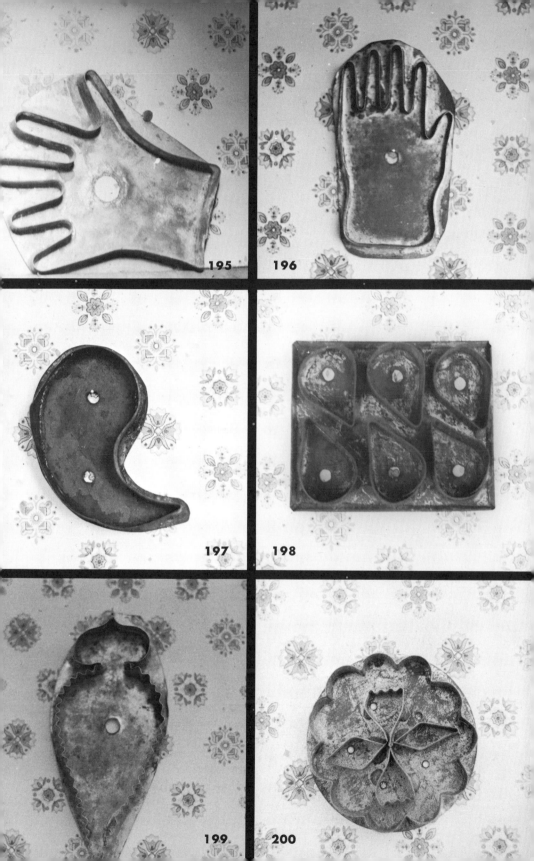

195

196

197

198

199

200

201—Diamond

202—Serated edge diamond with heart insert

203—Serated edge oval with insert of lillies

204—Unidentified

205—Serated edge circle

206—Serated edge square with heart insert

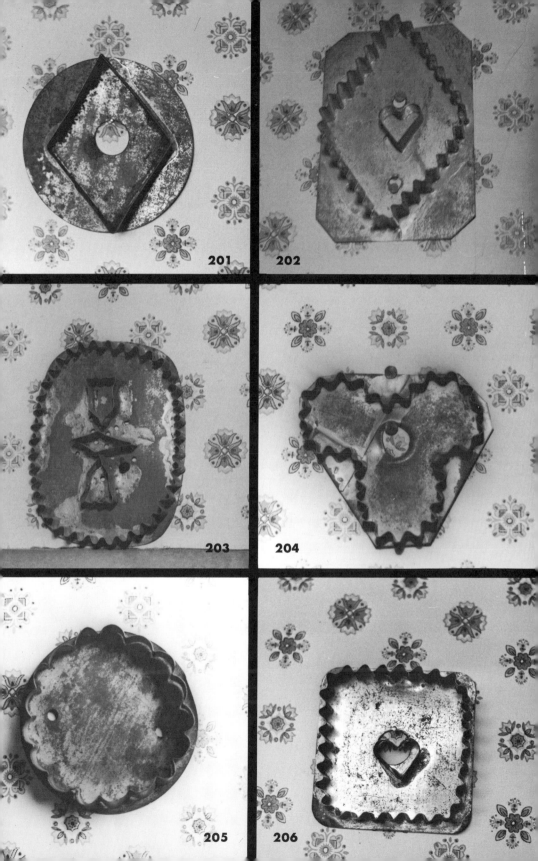

201

202

203

204

205

206

207—Unidentified

208—Unidentified serated edge oval with insert

209—Cookie board with miniatures

210—Closeup of 209 showing doll cutter bearing the stamped name of C. Snell—presumably of Reading

211—Cookie cutter bearing name of "Davis Baking Powder"

212—Cookie cutters bearing names of "Fries" and "Kreamer"

207

208

209

210

DAVIS KING POWDER

211

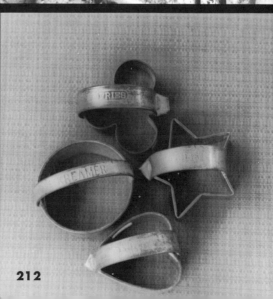

212

213—Cutter S shaped used, we are told, for making spreads using a cinnamon pastes.

214—Tin pattern used for Reindeer Cookie Cutters for about 67 years by tinsmith in Pennsylvania Dutch area and cut over pattern of his grandfather to assure authenticity and to save the original model which was made in 1830. He was fourth generation to practice this craft.

215—Tin pattern for Santa Cookie Cutter

216—Tin pattern for Rocking Horse Cookie Cutter

217—Tin pattern for Cookie Cutter for a small unidentified animal

218—Tin pattern for Turkey Cookie Cutter

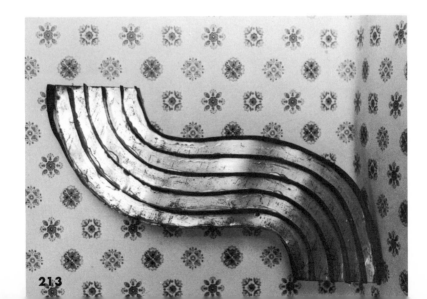

213

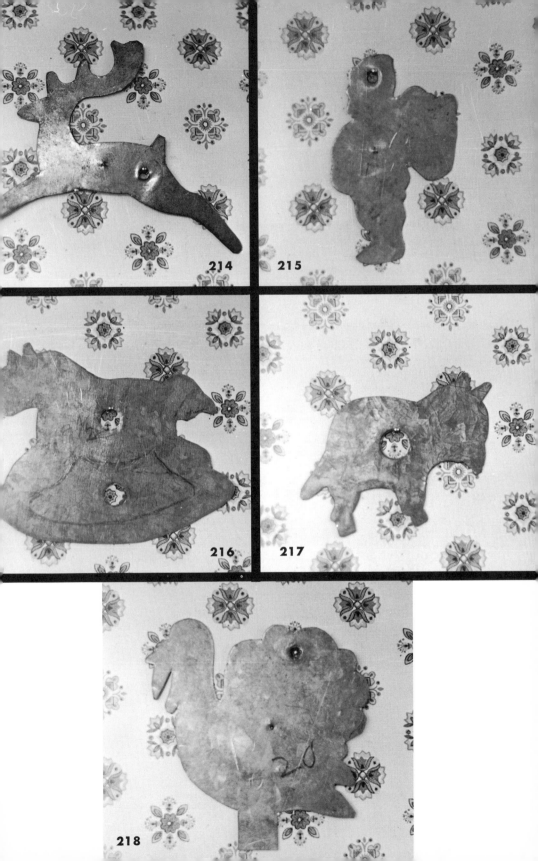

214

215

216

217

218

219—Tin pattern for a Victorian Lady Cookie Cutter

220—Tin pattern for an Angel Cookie Cutter—The notation on pattern of 23"—indicates the length of tin will be required to make the cutting edge.

221—Tin pattern for Christmas Tree Cookie Cutter

222—Tin pattern for Eagle Cookie Cutter

223—Tin pattern for Pitcher Cookie Cutter.

Since this will give the student an idea as to the method usually employed for this craft we will then digress and show patterns really prefered for making cookie cutters since they are more solid, will not bend as easily and will permit bending the tin cutting edge more accurately.

224—Wooden pattern for a Fish Cookie Cutter

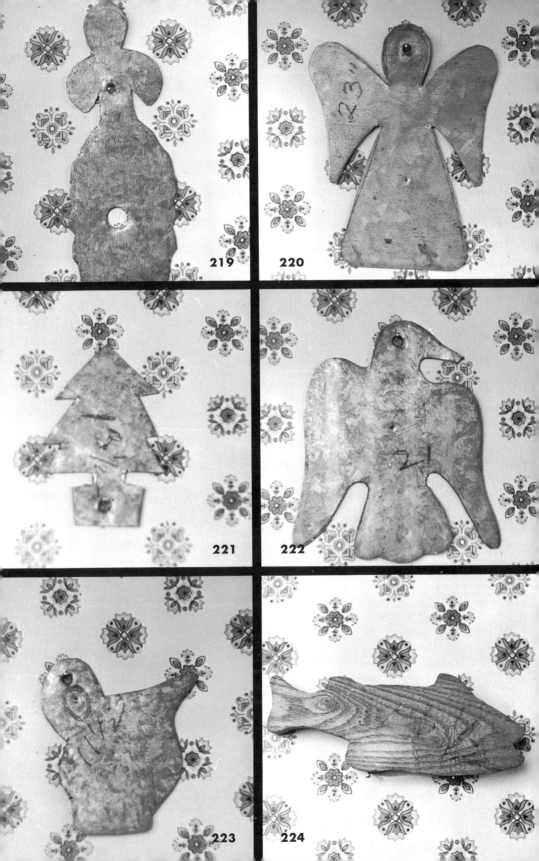

219   220

221   222

223   224

225—Wooden pattern for Twin Girls Cookie Cutter, and bearing the notation that it will require 15 inches of cutting edge to complete.

226—Wooden pattern for Tulip Cookie Cutter

227—Wooden pattern for Heart Cookie Cutter

228—Wooden pattern for Boot Cookie Cutter

229—Wooden pattern of Man Cookie Cutter

230—Wooden pattern for Star Cookie Cutter

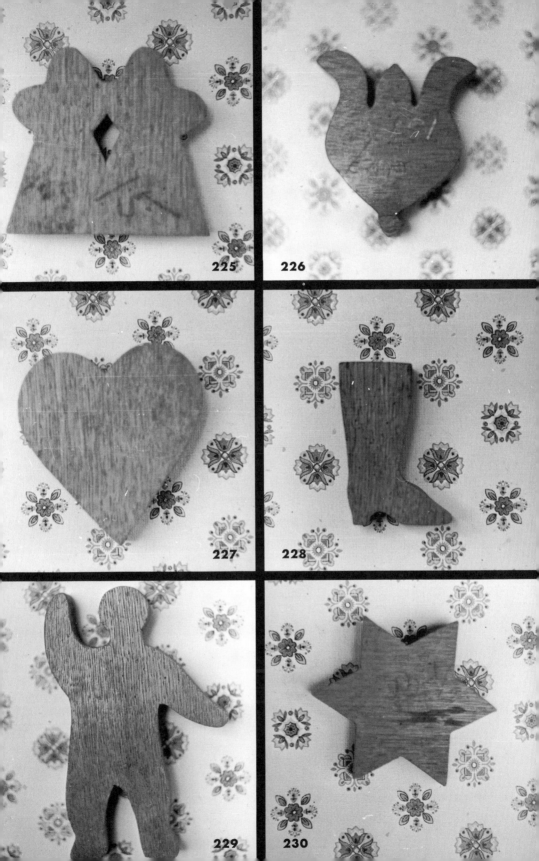

225

226

227

228

229

230

231—Wooden pattern for Tulip Cookie Cutter.

232—Wooden pattern for Eagle Cookie Cutter.

233—Wooden pattern for Dog Cookie Cutter.

234—Wooden pattern for Hand Cookie Cutter.

235—Wooden pattern for Rooster Cookie Cutter.

236—Wooden pattern for an intricate Christmas Tree Cookie Cutter.

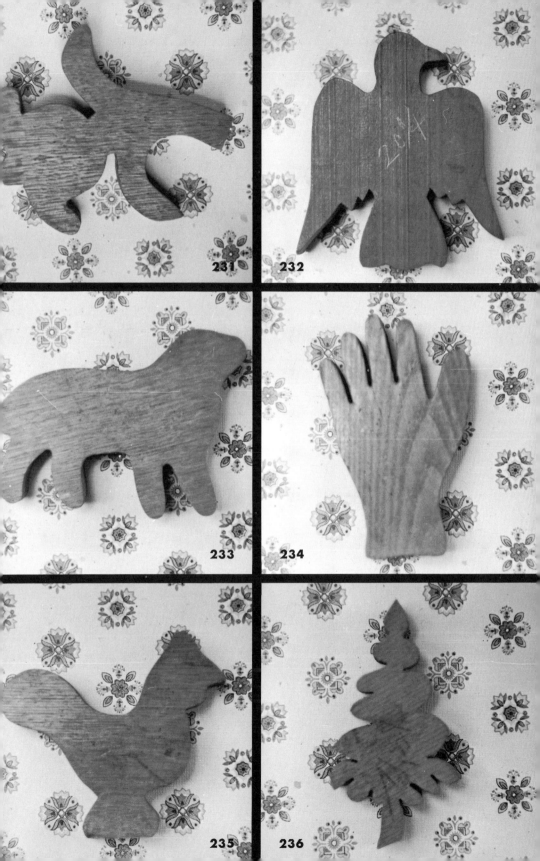

231   232

233   234

235   236

237—Wooden pattern for Horse Cookie Cutter and as will be noticed these Wooden patterns are all of Oak wood, a hard wood that will take a lot of punishment.

238—Tin pattern used for Quilting and dating back to about 1830—One of the original patterns.

239—Thin Wooden pattern used, we are told, for quilting.

240—Tin Spread pattern, early 19th century for further comparison.

241—Tin Spread pattern, early 19th century.

242—Tin Spread pattern, early 19th century, as above but larger.

237 238

239 240

241 242

243—Tin Spread pattern, as above.

244—Tin Spread pattern, as above but larger.

245—Tin Spread pattern, as above.

246—Tin Spread pattern, as above.

247—Tin Spread pattern, as above.

248—Tin Spread pattern, as above.

243   244

245   246

247   248

96

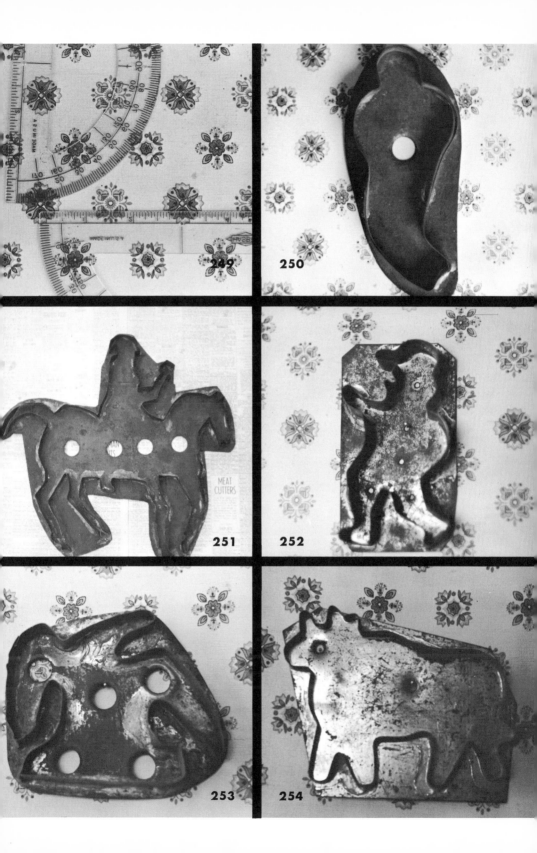

249

250

251

MEAT
CUTTERS

252

253

254

255—Rooster
256—Jug

98

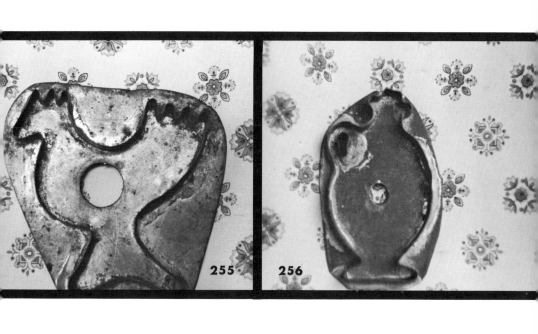

255   256

Turk's Head Molds

In 1894 Mrs. Grace Townsend produced the revised edition of the "Imperial Cook Book" and she referred to it as a monitor for the American housewife in the dining room and kitchen.

This cook book contains suggested "Bills of Fare"—instructions for dyeing or coloring—perfume and toilet recipes—laundry instructions and suggestions—simple suggestions for the nursery—suggestions for feeding invalids—it was an attempt, and a good one, to be of assistance to wives when these individuals, who were alone, who had no telephone, no means of communication, and possibly no close neighbors, might have to meet emergencies, or might need advice or assistance.

Among other listings it contained a list of articles necessary for the kitchen and laundry and following the bread knife, the potato masher, the stove, the coal shovel, the coal hod, etc. we find listed two cake pans, two sizes—four bread pans—two square biscuit pans—one set of jelly cake tins—four pie pans—two pudding molds, one for boiling, one for baking —two jelly molds, two sizes, etc.

Quite early our forefathers recognized that food should be as inviting in appearance as it was appetizing in taste and they seem to have paid quite a bit of attention to molds for this reason.

We had been, of course, prepared for this when we found the report of Alice Morse Earle—page 152—Home Life in Colonial Days—1898— Grosset & Dunlap-Publishers—that as early as the Colonial Days even their cakes, pies and puddings were most complicated and humble households were lavish in the various kinds they manufactured and ate.

Mrs. Townsend does not tell the housewife what type, kind or size of molds to secure. This is apparently left to the advice of friends, relatives, custom, preference, or possibly this was one of the popular gift items of that period.

She does, however, in her recipe for "Angel Food" cake caution that it is best to bake this in a "Turk's Head". You, she adds, can then rest it on the tube. Take it from the oven, turn pan upside down on a rest, and let it stand until the cake falls out.

In the tenth of her suggestions for aiding the housewife to become a successful cake baker she advises that a loaf cake baked in a tube pan bakes more evenly and if you are where you cannot secure a tube pan, she advises, you can improvise one by greasing a baking powder can placing it in the center.

There are many cook books available that are probably as practical and helpful but this one was close at hand and seemed to embody the main points we desired to illustrate.

The molds she refers to are called Angel Food cake molds, they are referred to as Turk's Head molds, they are referred to as Sponge Cake molds, more recently they have been called Swirl molds and sometimes

Bundt cake pans due possibly to its occasional use in baking Pound cakes, although probably there are many more such descriptive names for this interesting mold.

It however raises questions as to:

Who made the first such mold?

When was the first one made?

Where was the first one made?

For what purpose actually was the first one made?

What is or was the purpose of the funnel in its original conception?

Upon inquiry we were told that the purpose was so that upon completion of the baking the cake pan could be turned upside down on a bottle until the cake would fall off and Mrs. Townsend seems to confirm this.

We recently came across an article which seems to give another reason or explanation for the same process. In this article the author gives a recipe and describes a Sponge Cake which a friend of hers suggested that she bake. She then tells us that you pour it into an oiled and floured cake tin. (The angel food type of cake tin with a funnel in the middle) she tells us, etc. In describing the results, however, it seems not to have been up to expectations. It had fallen, and she wrote her friends for further instructions.

The reply indicated that it was due to the fact that she had failed to turn the cake upside down, after first taking it from the oven. In fact, the advice continued it should be left in this upside down position for an hour.

While the variety of Turk's Head molds is limitless there are many on which the funnel is closed and these resourceful individuals must have had means other than a bottle when required in order to rest it as instructed.

Some of these molds are only about 2 inches high and while we are certain that the even distribution of heat was one of the reasons for the early and higher molds having a funnel, many times it seems that the funnel must have been added merely for the decorative effect and we believe that a study of some of the molds, their style, their body composition, will confirm this.

In fact in recipe #48, page 19, Desserts by Alice Bradley—M. Barrows & Co.—Boston, 1930 we find that a small Angel cake pan is recommended for Chocolate Cottage Pudding.

Illustrations M1-M2 and M3 in the DIDEROT ENCYCLOPEDIA—Recueil de Planches Sur Les Sciences, Les Arts Liberaux Et Les Arts Mechaniques, Paris, 1762-1777 indicate the type of ovens in which these molds were used in and about this period and that molds such as cookie cutters, fish shaped molds and Turk's Head molds, pie plates, etc. were commonplace in 1762-1777.

The molds pictured seem to have been made of tin and this seems quite probable since it is a matter of record that this metal was available in this country since 1720 and abroad in or about 1650, and we understand that in the late 18th century copper and brass was replaced by cast iron, so

Cuisinier Patissier Traiteur Rotisseur
Tour à Pâte-Bassines, Mortier &c.

M 1

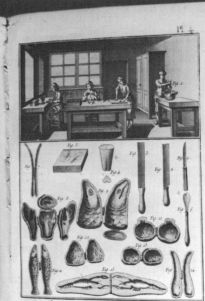

Confiseur, Pastillage et Moulles pour les Glaces

M 2

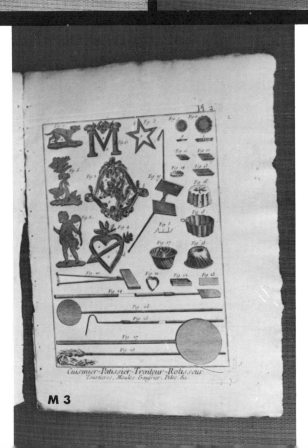

Cuisinier-Patissier-Traiteur-Rotisseur
Tourtieres, Moules, Gaufrier, Peles &c.

M 3

that, even copper and brass were available in quantity during the 18th century.

Beatrice Farnsworth Powers and Olive Floyd in Early American Decorated Tinware—1957—Hastings House, New York give credit to Shem Drowne of Boston as being the first tinsmith in the United States when he operated in 1720. They tell us that the Pattison factory was the one which was opened in Berlin, Connecticut about 1740 and that the manufacture here was very extensive and that they toward the end of the 18th century supplied the great part of the United States with their products, which included lanterns, candlesticks, candle molds, pie plates, cooky cutters, bread and cake pans, cannisters, etc.

It therefore seems that one of the first materials used to make funnel pans in this country was tin, but since this material was used for well over a century, the weight, the workmanship and other methods must be used to arrive at an approximate period for each individual item. It would be impossible to generalize on dates.

Tray—M 4—is a heavy gauge metal tinned and could quite possibly have been produced about this early period.

Pie Plates—M 5—early 19th century, no doubt, but have the same characteristics as these in Fig. 10—Plate 2—Illus. M 3.

Mold—M 6—a 20 fluted tin pan $1\frac{1}{2}$ inches high by $7\frac{1}{2}$ inches diameter— the plain funnel is 3 inches high.

Mold—M 7—a square plain $7\frac{1}{2}$ inch pan 3 inches high with a 4 inch high funnel 2 inches diameter at base, made of a heavy gauge tin, and with a small loop for hanging for convenience or for its slight decorative value.

Mold—M 8—a 9 inch wide octagonal shaped mold 2 inches high with plain sides, a 3 inch high funnel and with three flutings running around the base to give top of cake three convex circles for additional decorative effect, a medium weight of tin.

Mold—M 9—star shaped tin mold—six pointed—9 inch overall width by $2\frac{1}{4}$ inches high, plain sides, plain bottom and plain $2\frac{1}{2}$ inch high funnel, an extremely heavy gauge metal.

M 4

M 5

M 6

M 7

M 8

M 9

Mold—M 10—extremely heavy gauge tin pan—9½ inches diameter by 3¼ inches high—15 V shaped flutings around sides and bottom of pan turning somewhat to the left—a 46 fluted top rim—a plain 3½ inch high funnel—2¼ inches diameter at base, and with a small loop for hanging.

Mold—M 11—8½ inch tin mold 12 flutings form sloping sides, base is plain and 4¼ inch high funnel is plain—crudely, heavy gauge tin and seemingly early type.

Mold—M 12—heavy tin 6½ inches diameter by 3½ inches deep—plain top border—23 V shaped flutings around side and 12 leaf shaped depressions in bottom—3¼ inch high funnel closed at top.

A study of the copper molds in our collection, tin lined, shows that they were formed in two parts and that the two halves were joined in a square dovetailed manner commonly referred to as the "Wall-of-Troy" pattern which we believe is the mark usually used to determine that it was of American manufacture and these are we believe usually circa 1800.

Mold—M 13—copper, as above, 45 V shaped flutings around top rim, 6 lilly leaves running straight down funnel, across base and up sides to rim, plain top of funnel, 14 pointed star in top of funnel, inside of mold tinned, funnel and outside of mold joined as above by brazing with brass, a small loop for hanging, 10 inch diameter by 3¾ inch high with a 4¼ inch high funnel which has a diameter of approximately 3 inches at base.

Mold—M 14—10 inch diameter by 4 inches deep, heavy copper mold—51 V shaped flutings around top rim—8 leaf shaped depressions running from near top of funnel across bottom to bottom edge of side where a cathedral type of fluting surrounds the depression two deep until it reaches the V shaped fluted edge, 4½ inch high funnel by 2½ inch diameter at bottom. X shaped cross piece at top of funnel for strength. Inside tinned—joined as above—small loop for hanging.

Mold—M 15—early 19th century Pennsylvania Pottery cake mold—unusual Lilly pattern—the flower forms the funnel, it is 2¾ inches high by about 2¼ inches diameter at base—the flower extends to approximately the center of base and here a rim forms the dividing line where the 4 Lilly leaves that are in the decorative side treatment, and the fluted decorative dividers between them, join the Lilly. Mold is 8½ inches diameter by 2½ inches high, beautifully glazed and three rough spots on bottom where the bit stones supported it in drying. Small hole in top of funnel.

M 10   M 11

M 12   M 13

M 14   M 15

Mold—M 16—5½ inch diameter by 2 inch high cake mold with 10 concave flutings down the side—plain base and a plain funnel 3 inches high—early brown pottery mold of reddish clay with a dark brown glaze inside and on the sides outside, base outside is unglazed, open funnel.

Mold—M 17—9 inch diameter mold by 3½ inches high—brown pottery—20 convex flutings around inside on a slant to the left and the outside has 20 concave flutings to conform exactly. The shaping was carried right through the body. There is a small plain rim at top edge. The base inside has two concave flutings running around the base for decorative effect and the closed funnel is about 2½ inches high so that if the cake rises to any degree it will cover the funnel. Unglazed bottom is charred from use but the inside of funnel is a light cream color and seems almost to be of a fire clay type of composition. Unusual also in that it has two handles.

Mold—M 18—8¼ inch diameter mold with 17 flat sides at outer edge of top, the inside top edge is round, a greenish brown glaze, top inside edge plain and from here 17 V shaped flutings go straight down the side, across the bottom and partially up the funnel. The funnel itself is 3¼ inches high and the bowl height is 3¾ inches high. An ear at the side of bowl is meant to take a cord or hook to hang for decorative effect and convenience.

Mold—M 19—7 inch diameter mold with nine sides—9 heavy swirls to the right from top inside edge to base of funnel and outside edge has the reverse to conform—(The molding went completely through the body of the mold)—2¼ inch high funnel open at top, heavily glazed.

Mold—M 20—10 inch—7¼ inch—6 inch and a 3¼ inch conventional pottery molds with usual swirled effect.

Mold—M 21—yellow 7¼ inch diameter mold by John Bell, extremely heavy swirl, only 3 swirls given to this boldly conceived mold. Swirl extends from top edge to top of funnel in one continuous sweep. 4½ inch funnel on a 3⅝ inch high mold.

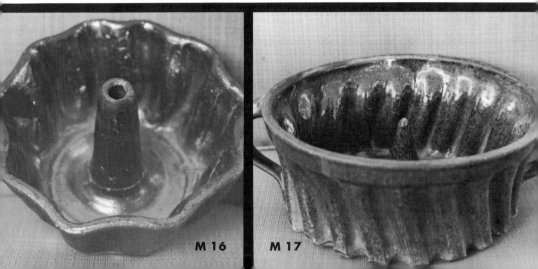

M 16   M 17

M 18

M 19

M 20

M 21

Mold—M 22—9½ inch diameter by 4¼ inch deep dark brown pottery mold—48 V shaped flutings around top rim—8 leaf shaped depressions extremely similar to M 14—4 inch high funnel.

Mold—M 23—9¼ inch brown pottery mold—7 heavy V shaped dividers mark 7 pieces of cake when baked and each division has a small ⅝ inch pyramid in center to mark, apparently, where the cherry, or other fruit decoration or delicacy should be placed. Two inch high mold with a 2¼ inch high funnel. Only inside of mold glazed, outside in original unglazed condition.

Mold—M 24—9½ by 7½ by 2½ white pottery mold and a 6½ by 5½ by 1¾ high white pottery mold made by "Copeland", each with identical swirls down the side and across the base—plain funnel, closed. These were no doubt meant to be used for puddings, since it would hardly stand the heat of baking.

Mold—M 25—6 by 4¼ by 2½ inch high mold with a 2 inch long funnel 1¾ inches deep in white pottery, made by "Copeland" and with 12 round depressions in bottom for cherry or similar fruit decoration when finished. Meant, like M 24, no doubt, for puddings and never intended for oven use. The funnel, apparently, was for decorative treatment.

Mold—M 26—7½ by 6½ by 5 inches high mold in white pottery with 3½ inch long by 3¼ inch deep funnel. Eight molded effect decorative treatments spaced evenly along side with rounded effect at base between each column seemingly to give the pudding a cathedral effect.

Mold—M 27—7½ inch diameter by 3¼ inch high grey Agateware mold with a 3¼ inch high funnel. Sides have an S shaped swirl down and across base to funnel.

M 22

M 23

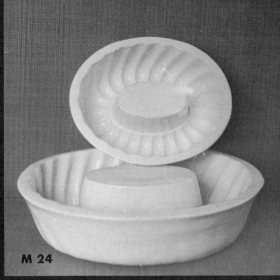

M 24

M 25

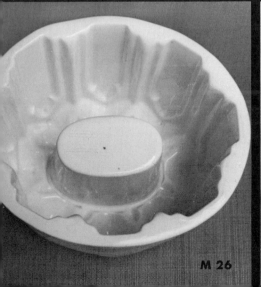

M 26

M 27

Mold—M 28—9¼ inch diameter by 4 inch high mold—blue Agateware outside—white enamel inside—16 V shaped flutings down side and across bottom in a slight angle to the right to base of funnel which is plain 3½ inches high.

Mold—M 29—9¾ inch diameter by 4 inch high mold—marked "Kreamer" #131—heavy tin—plain top border—32 V shaped flutings from this border to bottom of mold—bottom of mold has 16 walnut shaped depressions to give a design to top of cake—plain 4¼ inch high funnel by 4 inch diameter at bottom and 2¾ inch diameter at top.

Illus.—M 29A—top view of mold M 29 to indicate that the finished cake will be 9¾ inches diameter at bottom and 7½ inches at top and will have only a 1¾ inch wide circular top with a 4 inch open center.

Miss Bradley in "Desserts" page 190 tells us that a "Mary Ann Cake Pan" gives a cake with sides about 1½ inches high and an opening in the center 7 inches in diameter, or 8 inches square. She then gives instructions on how to fill and frost "Mary Ann Cakes,,' and she adds that the center may be filled with any gelatine dessert containing cream and she seems to be referring to a Bavarian Cream mixture which would be chilled and added shortly before serving—(she gives 7 recipes from Caramel Bavarian Cream to Pineapple Bavarian Cream)—or she adds the center may be filled with any filling—and here she gives suggested recipes from Almond Paste Filling to—(25 recipes later)—Raisin filling, Sour Cream filling, Strawberry whip, etc.

Since it is apparent that a "Mary Ann Cake Pan" is essentially a ring mold and since an Orange Mary Ann Cake is baked using a Sponge Cake recipe as a base it becomes apparent that these center openings were in some cases filled in similarly, in fact we are advised that in Sponge Cake, Angel Food Cake and Chiffon Cake it is quite frequently filled with a Bavarian Cream mixture or with whipped cream and strawberries.

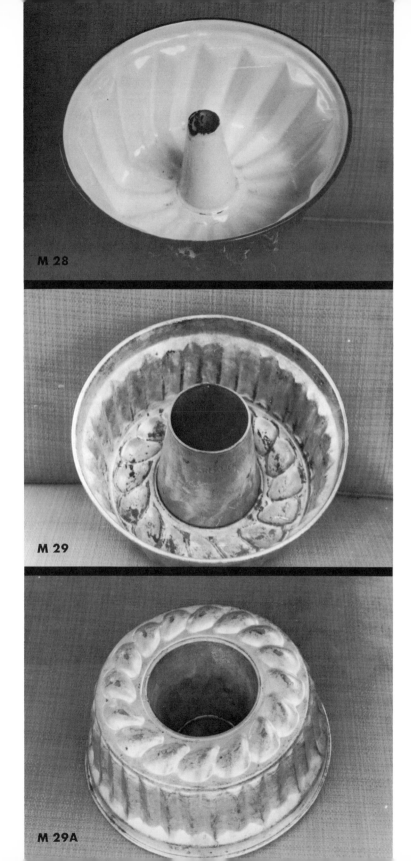

M 28

M 29

M 29A

Mold—M 30—9¾ inch diameter cast iron mold 4½ inches high—8 concave flutings from top edge straight down, across base and up funnel with V shaped flutings separating each concave area—inside of mold and outside are identical in design—weighs 9 pounds 9 ounces and while not marked is identical to some we have seen marked #965—Frank W. Hay & Sons—Johnstown, Pa.—Pat, March 10, 1891—(except the marked molds had a bail handle).

Mold—M 31—10½ inch by 4 inch high Porcelain mold—Gold decorated —15 V shaped flutings swirling in an S shape to the left from rim near top down across base and to top of funnel. Top rim has 15 curved segments of a completely different type for emphasis—4 inch high funnel—This was clearly a serving piece and of a decorative nature.

The term "Turk's Head Molds" according to Carl W. Drepperd in "A Dictionary of American Antiques" applies to metal or pottery baking dishes used to produce a cake swirled like a turban. He further tells us that these are really a form of mold, and *generally* with a funnel or vent in center.

Since "Turk's Head" was the term used to describe an ornamental knot, and since ladies frequently wore a headdress made to resemble or suggest the Oriental turban inspired by Sultan Muhammed in the late 18th century, and the early 19th century, this then may be the manner in which the term was first suggested.

Since these molds are, as indicated above, used for cakes and for puddings it is readily apparent that it is the shape rather than the use that determined the name and as Mr. Drepperd points out to us, there were many liberties taken with the shape that one becomes conscious that often the housewife wanted one that was different, one completely different from that of her neighbors so that, like her butter molds and cookies, the tasty cake which she baked for the church supper or the community affair would need no further identity, the shape told as plainly as though she had a large sign placed upon it that it was a product of her skill and knowledge.

There are, of course, plain cake pans with a plain tube and these are generally referred to as tube pans.

Mold—M 32—illustrates a "Swans Down Cake Pan" patented December 18, 1923 and made by E. Katzinger Co.—Chicago—Licensed Mfr.—It is a pan 9 inches in diameter by 3¾ inches high with a 4¾ inch high funnel by 1¾ inch diameter. A very heavy gauge of tin and with a slide on each of the two sides which can be raised to permit a knife to be inserted through the side wall opening to loosen the cake from the bottom of the pan.

M 30

M 31

M 32

Mold—M 33—9¼ inch diameter brown pottery mold by 3⅝ inches high —3⅜ inch high funnel, 3 inches diameter at base and 2 inches diameter at top which will produce a cake with sharply sloping sides and funnel and only about a 1 inch rounded top edge. Glazed inside walls and outside walls but not bottom edge or inside of funnel. This must have been meant for a filling in center from all appearances.

Mold—M 34—9¼ inch diameter clear "Glasbake" mold 3½ inches high —3¼ inch high funnel 2½ inch diameter at base and 1½ inch diameter at top—4 glass raised 1 inch long areas along top edge on which to rest the mold after baking and still to permit the air to escape.

Mold—M 35—8 inch diameter by 2¼ inches high tin mold—3¾ inch diameter funnel by 2⅝ inches high. Sides and funnel very nearly vertical and plain producing a ring type cake of the type as referred to in the "Mary Ann Cake" description. The only decorative feature is a Holly leaf and berry design impressed in the bottom of mold which will form the top edge upon completion. Has a ring for hanging on wall.

Mold—M 36—9½ inch long by 6½ inch wide tin mold 2 inches high with a 5½ by 2⅞ inch funnel 2¼ inches high—very similar to M 35 in all respects except it has no decoration anywhere—perfectly plain.

Mold—M 37—miniature 3¼ inch diameter by ¾ inch high tin mold with a ⅝ inch diameter by ¾ inch high funnel, closed—plain.

Mold—M 38—9½ inch diameter by 3¾ inches high—3 inch high funnel by ¾ inch funnel diameter—brown pottery glazed inside and outside—12 flutings around outside edge and across top to give a decorative effect, two handles at side.

M 33

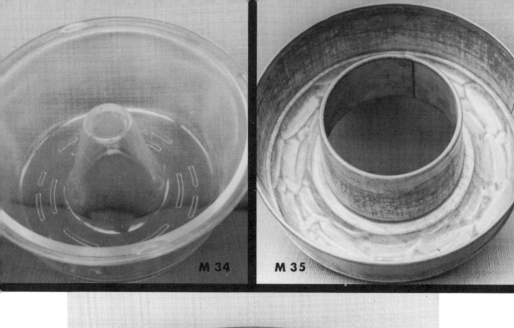

M 34

M 35

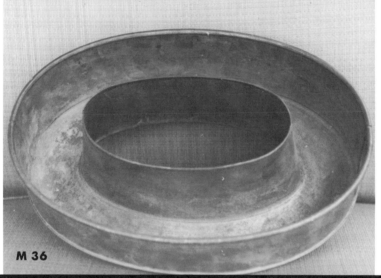

M 36

M 37

M 38

Mold—M 39—tin 7¼ inches diameter by 5½ inches high with 5¼ inch high closed funnel—13 flutings around sides and 16 diagonal flutings on top to add decorative value—has a tin lid which locks on top with pins.

Mold—M 40—tin 8 inch diameter by 3 inches high—2½ inch funnel 1¼ inches diameter at top—16 V shaped flutings run diagonally down side and swirls across top to plain funnel.

Mold—M 41—tin 8 inch diameter with plain sides 1⅛ inches high to a semi circular and diamond pillar effect 1 3/16 inches high which then terminates in a top consisting of 8 hearts and 8 domes between—has a 2½ inch high funnel by 3 inches diameter—very ornamental—has a ring to hang on wall. Outside view.

Mold—M 41A—inside view of M 41.

Mold—M 42—tin—extremely plain—9½ inches diameter by 1⅞ inches high with a 2⅛ inch high funnel 2¾ inches diameter at top—rounded top edge *but otherwise plain.*

Mold—M 43—tin—very similar to M 39—also with a tin lid but no funnel—6 inch diameter by 4½ inches high but still has a decorative pear impressed on top.

118

M 39

M 40

M 41

M 41A

M 42

M 43

Mold—M 44—white pottery—8¾ inches long by 6¾ inches wide—4 inches high with a lily and morning glory embossed effect—very decorative.

Mold—M 45—muffin pan—pottery—for 8 cup shaped muffins and a heart shaped muffin.

Mold—M 46—muffin pan—Iron—for 6 heart shaped muffins and a 6 pointed star muffin.

Mold—M 47—13 by 5¾ inch Iron pan for corn muffins.

Mold—M 48—10 by 5¼ inch Bread Pan—fluted.

Mold—M 49—white Pottery Mold similar to M 24—8½ by 5¼—3¾ inches high—Rabbit.

120

M 44   M 45

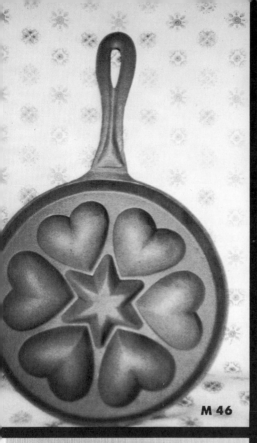

M 46

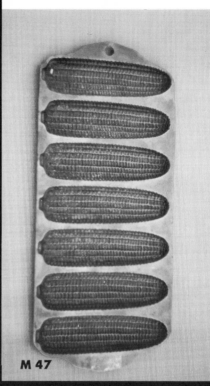

M 47

M 48

Mold—M 50—tin—triangular fluting around sides—pineapples and vegetables raised on top decoration.

The credit generally is given to the Roman period as the time when the Turk's Head mold was first made and used and from there it was adopted by all German speaking nations but it is indeed strange that this item so well known to all, so well accepted and used could have such an unknown background and be accepted over the centuries with no thought or record having been made, as far as we have been able to learn, as to its origin.

While a large cake will bake better and more evenly in a Turk's Head Mold many recipes of similar ingredients recommend a loaf or similar type pan. And while the smaller Turk's Head Molds do not require the funnel for heat distribution, the size of the funnel, the use of material which will not stand the heat of an oven, as well as the highly decorated ornamentation on many indicate the many uses to which this mold is now utilized and that it seems largely to fill a decorative requirement.

The Copeland examples for instance—circa 1847-1867—could have been used, we are told, for jellies, blancmange, meat (mixed with aspic jelly) or it could have been used for a flan in which the centre section could have been filled with fruit or to make jelly with the centre used with ice cream, blancmange, fruit or other such delicacy. They could, he continues, have been used for puddings or for Calf's foot jelly which was popular during the 19th century and particularly recommended for invalids, but, whatever the resulting food or dessert, it had to be of a nature that had to "set" prior to being removed so as to receive the design and to show it to its best advantage the design intended when removed.

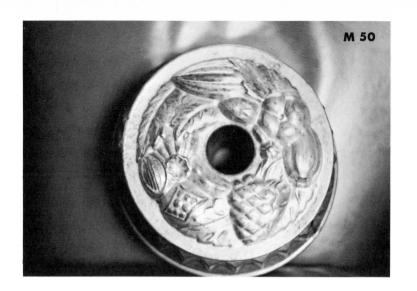

Butter Molds

Just like Cookie Cutters and Turk's Head Molds our forefathers decorated their butter to make it more presentable and appealing but additionally to show their identity with its manufacture without it being too obvious.

These molds were generally, but not always, made of wood—they were seldom marked with initials since modesty forbid such a practice and generally it was not resorted to—These molds were made in round shapes, as well as square, rectangular and we understand that they are found in oval, octagonal and triangular shapes as well. These resourceful individuals had a large variety of designs from which to select so that by a combination of design and unusual shape they had no difficulty in having their products recognized.

Since transportation was difficult, towns small, farms widely separated, the area was small, the opportunity for duplication in their area was extremely limited.

Molds for butter were made in one pound and fractional sizes so that there can be little doubt that the farmer planned to sell at least a portion of his supply and that this was a means of securing uniformity and ease of handling. The decorative value was an added and identifying touch.

Since the practice of using such molds has generally disappeared we will illustrate a few for the student to compare.

B 1—Glass—4 inch diameter by 2¼ inches deep—Cow design.

B 2—Wood—4½ by 2⅜ inch—W. F. initials—very old—Birch wood.

B 3—Wood—fluted edge—6¼ by 2½ inches by 1 inch deep—ornamental with initials D. F.

B 4—Wood—one half round—Sheaf of Wheat and initials W. K.—6½ inches long by 3⅛ inches wide by 3¼ inches deep.

B 5—Wood—4⅜ inch diameter—Eagle with Star.

B 6—Wood—4⅜ inch diameter—Eagle with Star—different spread of wings from above.

126

B 1   B 2

B 3

B 4

B 5　　B 6

B 7—Wood—5 inch diameter—Eagle and shield—4 concentric circled border. Eagle grasping arrows.

B 8—Wood—3¼ inch diameter—Eagle.

B 9—Wood—3¼ inch diameter—Cow in a field.

B 10—Wood—1½ inch diameter by ⅞ inches deep—Cow.

B 11—Wood—4⅞ inches by 2¾ inch—Cow with bell.

B 12—Wood—3½ inch diameter by 1¼ inches deep—Rose.

128

B 7

B 8

B 9

B 10

B 11

B 12

B 13—Wood—1¼ by ½ inch deep—Rose.

B 14—Wood—4⅜ by 3⅜ inch—Pineapple.

B 15—Wood—3⅝ inch diameter—Tulip.

B 16—Wood—3⅝ inch Tulip with leaves.

B 17—Wood—3 inch diameter—Fish.

B 18—Wood—3¼ by 1¾ inch deep—Heart.

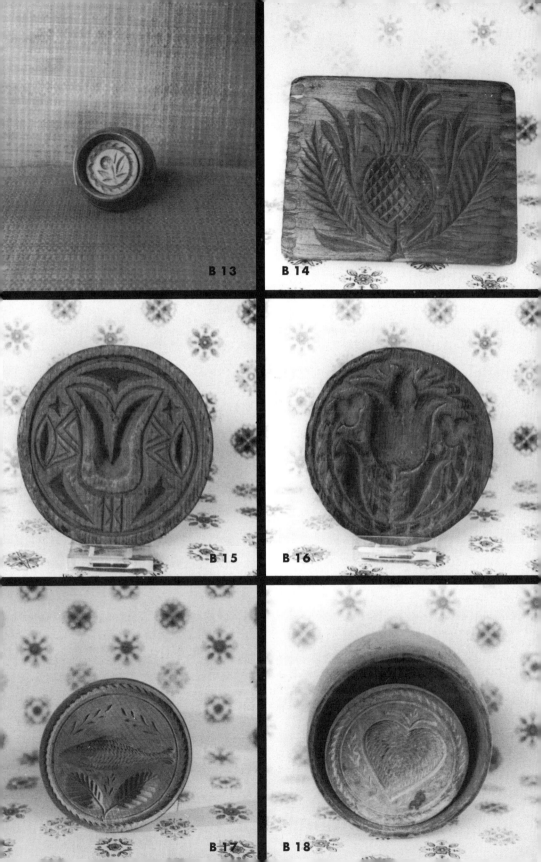

B 13

B 14

B 15

B 16

B 17

B 18

B 19—Wood—4 inch diameter—Swan.

B 20—Wood—3 inch Acorn.

B 21—Wood—2¾ inch diameter—Acorn.

B 22—Wood—4¼ inch diameter by 1⅞ inch deep—Oak Leaves.

B 23—Wood—3¼ inch diameter by 2 inches deep—Dahlia.

B 24—Wood—3 inch diameter by 1⅛ inch deep—same flower as above #B 23 but flower only, no foliage.

132

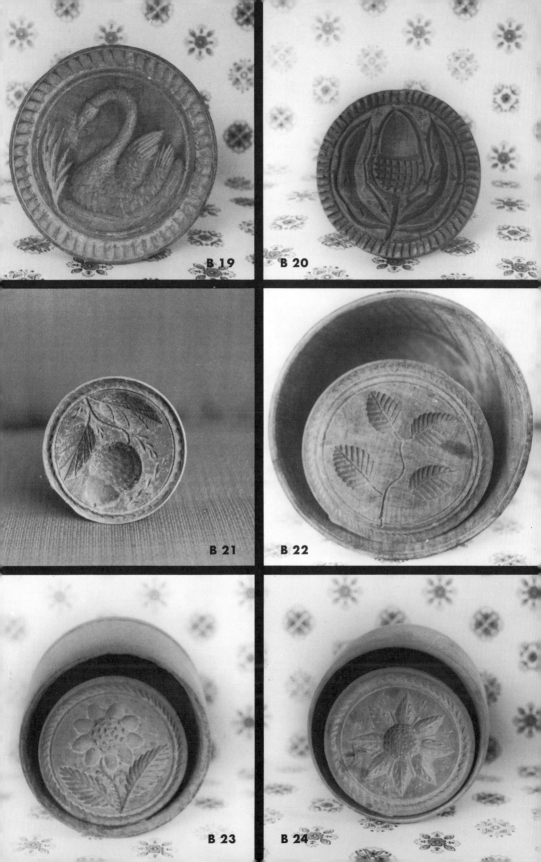

B 19

B 20

B 21

B 22

B 23

B 24

B 25—Wood—4¾ inch diameter—three leaves.

B 26—Wood—4½ inch diameter—Decorative and unusual.

B 27—Wood—4¼ inch diameter by 1¾ inches deep—Appears to be a Strawberry design.

B 28—Wood—4 inch diameter by 1¾ inch deep—Unidentified.

B 29—Wood—3½ inch diameter by 1½ inches deep—Unidentified.

B 30—Wood—4¾ by 2½ inches by 2¼ inches deep—seems similar to B 29.

B 25

B 26

B 27

B 28

B 29

B 30

B 31—Wood—3½ inch diameter by 1¼ inches deep—Could have been intended to be an Acorn—no name assigned.

B 32—Wood—4¾ inches by 2½ inches by 2⅜ inches deep—Spray.

B 33—Wood—2⅛ inch diameter—Fountain with 4 birds, one drinking, one spreading its wings and the two end birds looking toward their side in a sort of protective manner.

There are many additional designs but this will give the student an idea of the types and the subjects that may be encountered in his studies for comparative purposes, and permit him to have a starting point to add to.

It is extremely doubtful that these extend into the 20th century but the workmanship and originality used may help in analyzing further our heritage and is presented solely for this constructive purpose.

B 31

B 32

B 33

Ice Cream Molds

Cook books are among the more popular books purchased by our wives, mothers and sweethearts and the pride that they did and still take in their cooking and baking prowess more or less assures us that cookie cutters, Turk's Head molds and similar decorative accessories will continue to be used in some degree to add to the enjoyment of this delicacy where time is no factor and it is merely the pleasure that they derive from the finished product and the compliments that it evokes.

The Butter molds require additional time and are practically eliminated to keep production costs at a minimum and to attempt to retail the butter at the lowest and most competitive price possible—this is a business decision.

However, there is an additional mold which few remember since production costs have eliminated it some years ago—except for very few who still cater to the unusual.

This item is the Ice Cream Mold—a pewter mold—made in the latter part of the 19th century and the early part of the present 20th century—to enable ice cream manufacturers to make a special shaped confection for a special occasion, and the variety is very large.

These molds are in two and some in three parts hinged—the ice cream is placed in the mold which is closed and frozen hard—after the desired hardness has been attained it is removed, dipped quickly in warm water to remove the object molded and immediately placed upon a tray where it is re-frozen until delivery time. There is a large amount of labor involved and few manufacturers will today take the time to produce such an item and the costs really make the practice rather prohibitive.

The bust mold #1 (page 141) is marked 312 and bears the name impressed of V. CLAD & SONS—Phila. so that while we do not know the identity of this handsome individual with ribbons seemingly over his chest we do know that it was a professionally made mold which was not always the case.

If the ice cream manufacturer had the mold he would have to work the molding into his schedule and seldom promised delivery in less than about three weeks time. If, however, it had to be secured specially it would take additional time and the costs would have to include the cost of producing the mold which the manufacturer had no assurance that he would ever again require.

ICM 1—Pewter Mold—Man.

ICM 2—Pewter Mold—Victorian type tree with seeming Christmas ornaments or roses on it. Marked 115 and the name seems to be DADY.

ICM 3—Pewter Mold—Morning Glory—unmarked.

ICM 4—Pewter Mold—Lily.

ICM 5—Pewter Mold—Basket.

ICM 6—Pewter Mold—Pattie with "Bride and Groom" on top and along-
side is a wax copy of what the finished object would look like—
these copies were used as salesmen's samples.

140

ICM 2

ICM 3

ICM 4

ICM 5

ICM 6

ICM 7—Pewter Mold—a "Billiken" mold and a wax copy made with a similar mold but in a smaller size—shown together to give the student an idea of manner of production.

ICM 8—Wax objects made with pewter molds—a Lily made with Mold #4 and a "Liberty Bell".

ICM 9—Wax object made with a pewter mold—a "Morning Glory" made with Mold #3 and a "Sun Flower".

ICM 10—Wax object made with a pewter mold—a "Peach" with a portion removed to show the Stone—and a "Rooster".

ICM 11—Wax objects made as salesmen's samples—A "Dressed Chicken" and a "Pea Pod" with a portion removed to show the peas enclosed.

ICM 12—Wax salesmen's samples—Early War Veterans "Campaign Hat".

142

ICM 9

ICM 10

ICM 11

ICM 12

ICM 13—Wax "Santa Claus" salesmen's sample

ICM 14—Wax "Small Santa" and "Rabbit"

ICM 15—Wax "Christmas Tree"

ICM 16—Wax "Holly Branch"

ICM 17—Wax "Santa Claus"

ICM 18—Wax "Bride"

ICM 13

ICM 14

ICM 15

ICM 16

ICM 17

ICM 18

ICM 19—Wax "Groom"

ICM 20—Wax "Ring"

ICM 21—Wax "Rabbit and Mandolin"

ICM 22—Wax "Rabbit with guitar"

ICM 23—Wax "Rabbit with Cello"

ICM 24—Wax "Rabbit with basket tied on his back"

146

ICM 19   ICM 20

ICM 21   ICM 22

ICM 23   ICM 24

ICM 25—Wax "Harp"

ICM 26—Wax "Head and Musical instruments"

ICM 27—Wax "Tent and Small Sailboat"

ICM 28—Wax "Galley"

ICM 29—Wax "Sailboat"

ICM 30—Wax "Thimble" and "Pattie with Heart"

148

ICM 25

ICM 26

ICM 27

ICM 28

ICM 29

ICM 30

ICM 31—Wax "Heart with a Winged Cupid with his Bow and Arrow in firing position" and "Two Hearts and ribbon marked "Love"

ICM 32—Wax pattie with "Strawberry" and a pattie with "Three Roses"

ICM 33—Wax patties very decorative and otherwise unidentified

ICM 34—Wax "Lady"

ICM 35—Wax "Fan"

ICM 36—Wax "Clown"

150

ICM 33

ICM 34

ICM 35

ICM 36

ICM 37—Wax "Cannon" and individual seems to be a "Soldier"

ICM 38—Wax "Elephant"

ICM 39—Wax "Sheep" and "Tiger"

ICM 40—Wax "Cornucopia"

ICM 41—Wax "Bell" with a "Cupid holding his bow near the flame at an open fire"

ICM 42—Wax "Dirigible"

152

ICM 37

ICM 38

ICM 39

ICM 40

ICM 41

ICM 42

154

ICM 43

ICM 44

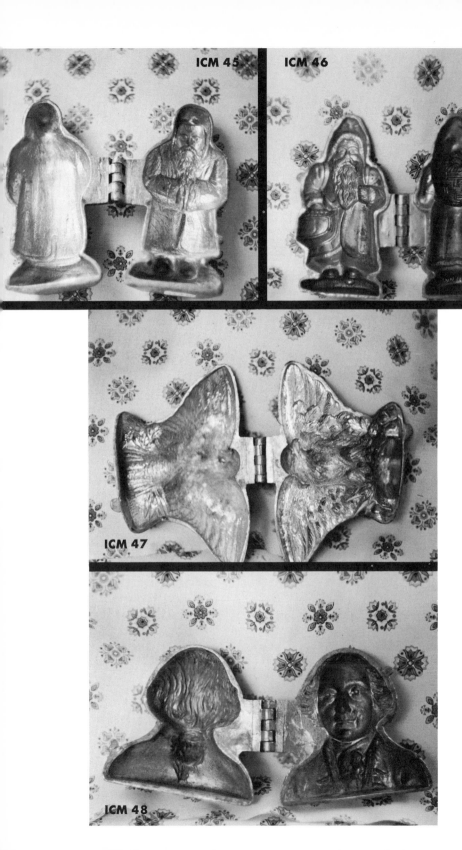

ICM 45 ICM 46

ICM 47

ICM 48

ICM 49—Galley Pewter Mold to produce item as #28. This mold is additionally marked "DESCOPRO". E. & Co.—dated 1896.

ICM 50—Stork Pewter Mold

The field for this type decorative favors for parties was limitless and for those who could not find what they wanted from stock or from salesmen's samples they could always be made up specially. If the success of a party depended on such a motif or favor there were always handy individuals who could and would produce them. The manufacturers of such molds were interested only in large scale production of most desired types of molds.

Symmetry

A splendid example of the folk art of the Pennsylvania Dutch is the sgraffito plate decorated with a two-headed eagle by Georg Huebner, probably of Montgomery County, Pennsylvania, for Katharine Raeder and it is such an outstanding example that it is constantly referred to in examining or studying our heritage.

No less interesting is the plate made by Samuel Paul for Maria Helbard along somewhat similar lines in 1798 and while sometimes these birds are referred to as doves it is generally conceded that they were double-headed eagles. In fact, Mr. V. Wheeler—Holohan—in Boutels Manual of Heraldry, Fred Warne & Co., London—1931, tells us that birds of prey are said to be displayed with expanded wings and those not birds of prey are displayed with wings disclosed. The two plates above referred to have their wings expanded, (spread wide).

He tells us also that one of the first methods of conjoining two coats of arms in heraldry was by dimidiation, which consisted of cutting two shields in halves along the palar line and joining the dexter half of the one to the sinister half of the other, thus forming one shield of the two. In this manner, for instance, the half of the husbands coat of arms was placed in the dexter—(the right)—side while the wifes coat of arms was placed in the sinister—(the left)—side.

This practice was introduced, he says, in the 14th century but was discontinued within a short time for it apparently led to some extraordinary results and he adds that Planche says that the double-headed eagle is a result of the practice of dimidiation. While this may have been the case, we believe, rather, that this creature was the result of the general practices, policies and rules which govern heraldry since dimidiation would not reverse the arms of either party but would merely substitute one half for another half in their otherwise normal positions.

Cleopatra's Needle, erected at Heliopolis by the Pharoh Thothmes III about 1500 B.C. and removed to Alexandria, The Royal City of Cleopatra, in the 18th year of Augustus Caesar, B.C. 12, and presently on the Victoria Embankment in London is guarded by a sphinx on either side facing the obelisk—one of the earlier examples of this plan of symmetry.

In the case—"The Treasure of the OXUS"—in the British Museum, London, are on display a large number of items of gold jewelry said to be from the city of Khandian or Kabodian to which special importance is attached since it incorporates many elements from the arts of Central Asia and Bactria in the 5-4th Century B.C. and among them is only one—number 116—an armlet decorated with opposed "Winged Persian Griffins". (The armlet seems to be about 4 inches inside length, three inches inside height, about $\frac{5}{8}$ inches thick and has two Griffins about two and one half inches tall facing one another. This then is another example, but one only of the

159

many shown, and indicates that this duplication in reverse was no general trend, practice, plan or policy.

In the "Far Eastern Art Room" number 44 of the Victoria and Albert Museum—London—will be found a number of "ORDOS" Bronzes, ornaments made in the Chinese-Mongolian border region in the 5-3 Century B.C. and among them number M 17 is an ornament approximately five by two inches consisting of two horses, head to head, both with head lowered eating, each identical with the other in reverse.

Also is shown number—M 160—about seven by three and one half inches having two figures in the center flanked on either side by a horse again each horse an exact duplicate of the other in reverse. Shown also is number—M 18—about eight by four inches of two roosters fighting, each wing, each head and each posture of the one is identical to the other but in reverse—again no trend or policy but percentage wise considerably more evidence of symmetry than shown in any of the above examples.

In the Victoria and Albert Museum—London—number—A 200—is a three foot by seven foot, approx., stone mosaic fragment of a pavement of the 2-3 Century A.D. probably from Carthage where the decorative treatment was symmetrical.

David Talbot Rice, Thames and Hudson, London, 1963, in "Art of the Byzantine Era" page 70 tells us that his example number 58 is a silk textile presently in the Vatican depicting a lion-hunt where the animals, birds, or riders were confronted with a tree and it is his manner of describing the symmetrical effect where the tree is in the center and the figures or objects are similarly placed on either side in reverse. This textile is attributed to Byzantium, eighth century, A.D.

In the 12th century there started a *system* of decoration on the continent and in Great Britain referred to as heraldry. They were at first very simple, some simply painted with one or more bands of color in vertical, horizontal or diagonal stripes and it became a matter of pride for the son to use the shield or a shield the emblem identical to, or similar to, the one borne by his father in some famous engagement, of these history conscious nations.

On page 4, Boutell's Heraldry by C. W. Scott—Giles, O.B.E. and J. P. Brooke—Little, F.S.A. in describing a shield of Geoffrey of Anjou, they advise that the shield is curved and that little more than half of it is visible but the visible portion contains four lions and therefore they may *assume* that two, or perhaps three, additional would be on the hidden portion. This was on a shield presented in 1127 A.D.

On page 19 they tell us that the shield has always been the principal object for the display of armorial bearings, whether in war or in tournament and as a result it has become closely associated with heraldry to the extent that centuries later the shield continues as the shape and figure in which arms usually appear.

They then advise that the form of the shield has strongly influenced heraldic design and that frequency of arms consisting of three charges being placed—two and one—was due to the shape of the shield.

The shield to which they refer, however, is not the round Greek shield, or the Norman shield but rather one with a flat top edge and a rounded bottom edge which may have been adopted, in reverse, from the arch in Gothic Architecture which started at or about 1160 A.D.

Since the shield was intended as a protector and since it was more frequently curved, identification was required from any forward angle and it was essential that either the right or the left half would identify the bearer and this probably caused the use of duplication and uniformity above referred to.

While supporters are constantly used in heraldry it will be observed that these figures which stand on either side of a shield, as if upholding and guarding it (be they angelic or Human beings, or any kind of living creature, natural or imaginary are nearly always shown in pairs and usually, but not always, alike.

The Victoria and Albert Museum contain an extremely large variety of plates of various sizes bearing a uniform treatment as we have described from England, Germany, Switzerland, Austria, Hungary, Central Europe, Italy, Persia and Turkey, etc. The last three named seem to date from the 16th and 17th centuries while the balance seem to date from the 17th and 18th centuries. Included is item number 80 bearing the "Arms of the Watermen's Company of London"—made in Bristol and dated 1716.

The King Edward VII Gallery of the British Museum concentrates in cases A, B & C of Row XXX a display of ceramics bearing the coats of arms of various individuals. There are 65 items varying from plates, cups and saucers, jars, bottles, etc. to tea pots and bear the arms from those of "Peter the Great of Russia" circa 1689 to those of the "Royal Arms of England from 1714-1801 resting on a trophy of Masonic Emblems."

No doubt, after $5\frac{1}{2}$ to 6 centuries of heraldic thinking Thomas Toft, Ralph Simpson—William Talor—Ralph Toft—Samuel Malkin and other 17th and 18th century potters were accustomed to such uniformity and in decorating a plate they added supporters, or duplicated in reverse on one side of a plate the design on the other side—a practice referred to after 1541 A.D., and 58 years after the forming of the College of Arms, as symmetry.

While the practice was seemingly not originated by the art of heraldry it was not widespread nor popular until arms bearing such a practice appeared more frequently and gave the stimulus to these artists as well as to the rural artists of our own country who performed their artistry on plates, blanket chests, song book title pages, book marks, birth certificates, manuscripts, pin prick pictures, etc. in and about the latter 18th and the early 19th centuries.

This was observed by Dr. Robacker, on page 10—Pennsylvania Dutch Stuff—where, in referring to the tree of life motif he tells us that *at the hands of the Pennsylvania artist* the tree was drawn as a straight central stem with curved branches or fronds on either side, sometimes so symmetrical as to suggest segments of concentric circles.

In volume 4—Cambridge Medieval History—Cambridge University Press—New York—1936—we find that in the period covered—(717 A.D. to 1453 A.D.)—the first use of the double-headed eagle as a symbol is ascribed to the Nicene Empire—(1206 A.D. to 1254 A.D.) and that Dusan had himself crowned at Skoplje in 1346 A.D. and introduced Byzantine emblems and customs; as Tsar he assumed the tiara and the double-eagle as the heir of the great Constantine.

The double-headed eagle therefore was known prior to the 14th century (and the start of dimidiation) and it was introduced in the early 13th century, about a century after the start of heraldry, so that it is quite conceivable that this strange creature was inspired by heraldry.

While sacred persons were usually represented by the emblems associated with them, as roses and lilies for the virgin, they resorted to symbols frequently. Pelicans are always depicted in a form more heraldic than natural, wheat, barley and other grain is commonly shown in the form of a sheaf which then presents a uniform appearance—the Fleur-De-Lis first appeared on a royal seal in 1137-80, again at the start of the period of heraldry, a cup was depicted as a goblet with stem and foot, a sheaf or bundle of arrows consists of three, usually, one erect and the others crossing in saltire, (a diagonal cross), all tied at the center, apparently again with the idea of uniformity.

The mermaids and the mermen were frequently subjects as well as the quatrefoil, cinquefoil, etc. identified by the number of leaves they bore, were common subjects.

The heart was identified for the first time in 1463 as "a symmetrical figure formed of two similar curves meeting in a point at one end and a cusp at the other" according to the Oxford Universal Dictionary. This was only 21 years prior to the forming of the "College of Arms" in 1484 and since it appears that the shape of a heart as presently used today on playing cards, valentines, etc. was originated at that early period it is entirely possible that this form, like many others we use today with no further thought, may be due entirely to heraldry.

In The V & A Museum—Room #135—Italian Maiolica 14 to 18 century is item #440, a plate, circa 1510—it is of earthenware from "Deruta" the decoration is two hands—(a mans and a womans)—with the coat cuff showing at the outer edge—The hands are clasped and above the hands is a copper lustre "strawberry"—it has all of the characteristics of a strawberry—it has the identical shape—it has a three leaf hull showing on top, but, the strawberry is pierced by three blue arrows.

One pierces the object from an area best described by the use of the face of a clock as from 10 to 4—one from 9 to 5—and one from 2 to 7—this then in 1510 in Deruta was the artists conception of a heart.

Austrian Professor Haberlandt remarked that rural art is by no means an underdeveloped or discarded art but rather a branch of art in general and he adds that ancient traditions and even prehistoric influences can be traced in it so that an ancient heritage has been faithfully preserved.

In European Ceramic Art—page 483—William B. Honey tells us that though in general independent, the art of the peasant-potter commonly reveals an ancestry.

In the preface to A Manual of Heraldry Historical and Popular by Charles Boutell, M.A. dated 1863 but appearing in the Wheeler-Holohan —1931 issue Mr. Boutell tells us that he has been content to refer only incidentally, and in a few words, to the value and interest of heraldry as a handmaid of history, as an ally of art, and the chronicler of archaeology.

The decorations therefore on the 18th and early 19th century objects made by our forefathers then showed the same background and heraldic influences.

We attach a picture—(Fig. 1)—of a 14 inch tin glazed plate which has a double-headed pelican wearing a crown and while we have been unable to have it identified as to country, potter or date it will immediately explain what we have in mind.

Fig. 2—is the mark of the potter or the decorator of number 1 and of number 3.

Fig. 3—is another 14 inch plate by the same potter but is pictured only to indicate the uniformity, the symmetry we have been referring to.

Fig. 4—a pin prick picture from the early 19th century and we find again a uniformly shaped charger, or central item used and the tulips and foliage are duplicated identically in reverse.

Fig. 5—by Martin Brechall is self explanatory.

Fig. 6—by F. Krebs is self explanatory.

164

Fig. 1

Fig. 2

Fig. 3

Fig. 4

Fig. 5

Fig. 6

Fig. 7—by F. Hartman of Libanon—(sic) is self explanatory.

Fig. 8—by G. Bauman of Ephrata is self explanatory.

Fig. 9—will indicate that on occasion a liberty was taken but it is rarely a departure—only a token show of independence. Observe that while the balance is duplicated the two tulips at the bottom are not the exact center nor are they the same size.

Fig. 10—is a 16½ inch plate made in Staffordshire, ENGLAND and which follows a similar uniformity but with the red and the yellow tulips alternating around the rim and with a canoe—(again a uniform object)—and an individual standing in it playing the violin as the center theme.

When Mr. Boutell continues to tell us that to illuminators heraldic opens a wide and richly diversified field of attractive study he is referring to the Gothic type-face for which we are also indebted to this era and a study of 18th century books and bindings in the library of the British Museum will reveal a large group with symmetric illumination and with frequently coats of arms on the cover in gold.

The beautiful and deservedly popular art of illuminators find in heraldry a most versatile and efficient confederate, he tells us, and true illumination is indeed, in its nature heraldic; the true heraldry provides for illuminators the most appropriate, and effective patterns both of their subjects and the details and accessories of their practice.

It is apparently to this era and these allied practices that we are indebted for much of the art work so highly prized today as well as for many of the symbols we constantly use with no thought as to origin and a thorough study of this interesting subject would, we believe, prove to be extremely interesting and helpful.

Fig. 7

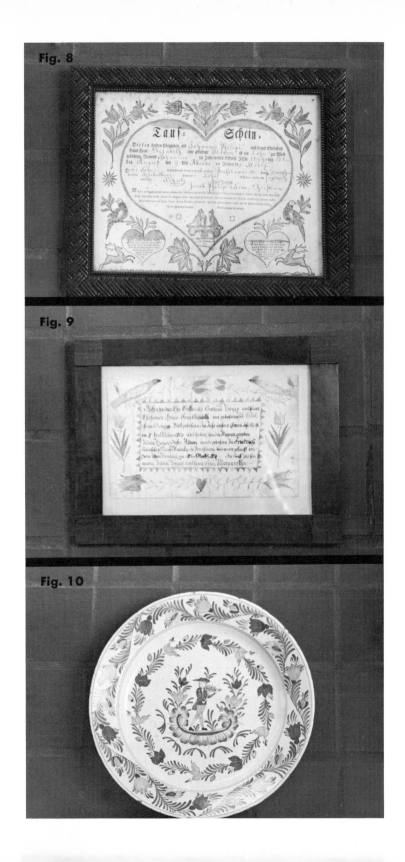

Fig. 8

Fig. 9

Fig. 10

BOOKS FOR REFERENCE AND STUDY

Antiques, December, 1923—Cover, page 286 and page 287.

Bjorn, Thyra Ferre—*Once upon a Christmas Time*—Holt, Rinehart and Winston—New York—1964.

Barret, Richard Carter—*Bennington Pottery and Porcelain*—Crown Publishers, Inc.—New York—1958.

Baud, Bovy Daniel—*Peasant Art in Switzerland*—"The Studio" Limited, London—1924.

Bradley, Alice—*Desserts*—M. Barrows & Company—Boston—1930.

Brooke, Little, F.S.A., F.H.S., J.P. and Scott, Giles, O.B.E., F.H.S., C.W. —*Boutell's Heraldry*—Frederick Warne & Co.—London & New York —1966.

Brown, Jr., Gordon B., Editor—*Beyond the Tinsel*—Valley Traveler— Valley Publishing, Inc.—December 1967—Volume 3—Number 4.

Chamberlain, Jacqueline—*Collecting Woodenware*—Western Collector— Volume 1 V—Number 7—July 1966—pages 8-9-10.

Christensen, Edwin O.—*The Index of American Design*—The Macmillan Company—New York—1950.

Clements, Laura Lee—*Food Molds for King and Peasant*—Western Collector—September, 1967.

Cole, Ann Kilborn—*From Old Christmas Trees*—Western Collector— December, 1967—pages 8-9-10-11.

Cooper, Ronald G.—*English Slipware Dishes*—1650 to 1850—Alec Tiranti Ltd., London—1968.

Crocker's, Betty—*Betty Crocker's Cooky Book*—Golden Press—New York —no date—circa 1963.

Devoe, Shirley Spaulding—*The Tinsmiths of Connecticut*—Published for the Connecticut Historical Society by Wesleyan University Press— Middletown, Connecticut—1968.

Diderot, Denis—*A Diderot Pictorial Encyclopedia of Trades and Industry* —Dover Publications—New York—1959.

Diderot Encyclopedia—Recuil de Planches Sur Les Sciences, Les Arts Liberaux Et Les Arts Mechniques, Paris, 1762-1777—page Pl.2.

Dolan, J. R.—*The Yankee Peddlers of Early America*—Bramhall House— New York—1964.

Drepperd, Carl W.—*A Dictionary of American Antiques*—Charles T. Branford Co.—Boston—1952.

Earle, Alice Morse—*Home Life in Colonial Days*—Grosset & Dunlap— New York—1898.

Ellison, B.Sc., J. Audrey—*The Great Scandinavian Cook Book*—Crown Publishers, Inc.—1967.

Elvin, Ella and Peterson, Alice—*The Sunday News Family Cook Book*—Rowman and Littlefield—New York—1962.

Escoffier, A.—*The Escoffier Cook Book*—Crown Publishers—New York—1941.

Family Circle—*Christmas Helps*—1967.

Farmer, Fannie Merritt—*The Boston Cooking School Cook Book*—Little, Brown & Co.—No date.

Floyd, Olive and Powers, Beatrice Farnsworth—*Early American Decorated Tinware*—Pond, Ekberg Company—Springfield, Mass.—1957.

Foley, Daniel J.—*Little Saints of Christmas*—Dresser, Chapman & Grimes, Inc.—Boston—1959.

Frame, Bert—*Original Pennsylvania Dutch Cookie Cutters*—No date.

Gould, Mary Earle—*Antique Tin & Tole Ware*—Charles E. Tuttle Co.—Rutland, Vermont—1958.

Graff, M. M.—*Facts and Fancies about the tree*—New York Times—New York—December 24, 1968—page 38D.

Griem, Breta, L. Keating, Ethel M.—*The Best from Midwest Kitchens*—and Lothe, Ada B.—Gramercy Publishing Co.—New York—1946.

Gullers, Av Ingvor Och Kw—*Jul*—P. A. Norstedt & Soners Forlag—Stockholm—1957.

Hadfield, Miles & John—*The Twelve Days of Christmas*—Cassell—London—1961.

Hole, Christina—*Christmas and its Customs*—M. Barrows & Company, Inc.—New York—1958.

Homan, Col. Wayne E.—*Holiday Cookie Cutters*—Hobbies—November, 1967—pages 98J-K-V-W.

Hylton, Bill—*Berks Tinsmith finds 83 time to retire*—Allentown Morning Call—Allentown, Penna.—November 7, 1968—page 51.

Inquirer, Philadelphia—*Yule 100 years ago*—Today section—Philadelphia—December 24, 1967—page 3.

Irving, Washington—*Old Christmas and Bracebridge Hall*—Macmillan and Co.—London and New York—1886.

Jenkins, Dorothy H.—*Antiques—Mementos of Victorian Christmases*—Woman's Day—December, 1967—page 37.

Kauffman, Henry—*Pennsylvania Dutch American Folk Art*—American Studio Books—New York—1946.

Kemmerer, Anne S. Museum—*Past Christmases Revived*—News item Sunday Call-Chronicle—Allentown, Penna.—December 17, 1967—page E-8.

Lestz, Gerald S.—*Zee Kauffman's Tree*—Lancaster New Era—Lancaster, Penna.—December 20, 1965.

Klees, Frederick—*The Pennsylvania Dutch*—The Macmillan Company—New York—1950.

Kovel, Ralph and Terry—*Know Your Antiques*—Crown Publishers, Inc.—1967.

Leighton, Frances Spatz—*Happy New Year at the Embassies*—Today—Philadelphia Inquirer Magazine—December 31, 1967—pages 3-4-5.

Lichten, Frances—*Folk Art of Rural Pennsylvania*—Charles Scribner's Sons, Ltd.—London and New York—1946.

Merkert, Tilde—*Witch Balls*—Spinning Wheel—January, February, 1967 pages 14-15-47.

Mitchell, Edward—*Household Library*—Five Volumes in one—R. Worthington—New York—1882.

Newsmagazine—*A Swedish Lucia Queen*—Scandinavian Times Newsmagazine, Copenhagen, Denmark—page 5—1967—no date.

Olssen, Marianne—*Christmas in Sweden 100 years ago*—Tre Tryckare—Goteberg—1965.

Page, Thomas Nelson—*Santa Claus's Partner*—Charles Scribner's Sons—New York—1899.

Pasley, Virginia—*The Christmas Cookie Book*—Little, Brown and Company—1950.

Peterson, Alice and Elvin, Ella—*The Sunday News Family Cook Book*—Rowman and Littlefield—New York—1962.

Piercy, Caroline B.—*The Shaker Cook Book—Not by Bread Alone*—Crown Publishers, Inc.—New York—1953.

Powers, Beatrice Farnsworth and Floyd, Olive—*Early American Decorated Tinware*—Pond, Ekberg Company—Springfield, Mass.—1957.

Rice, A. H. and Stoudt, John Baer—*The Shenandoah Pottery*—Shenandoah Publishing House, Inc.—Strasburg, Virginia—1929.

Rice, David Talbot—*Art of the Byzantine Era*—Thames and Hudson—London—1963.

Robacker, Earl F.—*Pennsylvania Dutch Stuff*—University of Pennsylvania Press—Philadelphia—1964.

Robacker, Earl F.—*Pennsylvania German Cooky Cutters and Cookies*—Mrs. C. Naaman Keyser—Plymouth Meeting, Penna.—1946.

Robacker, Earl F.—*Touch of the Dutchland*— A. S. Barnes and Co., Inc.—New York—1965.

Root, Waverly—*The Food of France*—Alfred A. Knopf—New York—1958.

Rushing, Lilith and Voss, Ruth—*Cake Cook Book*—Chilton Books—Philadelphia—1965.

Sandys, F.S.A., William—*Christmastide, its history, festivities, and carols*—John Russell Smith—London—E. Tucker—London—circa 1833.

Servicio Information Espanol—Spanish Information Service—#272—December 25, 1967—#273, January 1, 1968—#274, January 8, 1968 and #288, April 15, 1968.

Shelley, Donald A.— *The Fraktur. Writings or Illuminated Manuscripts of the Pennsylvania Germans*—The Pennsylvania German Folklore Society—Schlechter's—Allentown, Penna.—1961.

Stearns, Betty Dixon—*The Pot*—Boiler Column—The Crier—Florence, Italy—April, 1967—page 10.

Stoudt, John Baer and Rice, A. H.—*The Shenandoah Pottery*—Shenandoah Publishing House, Inc.—Strasburg, Virginia—1929.

Stoudt, John Joseph—*Early Pennsylvania Arts and Crafts*—A. S. Barnes and Co., Inc.—New York—1964.

Tait, Elaine—*Collector's Molds*—Philadelphia Inquirer Magazine—August 25, 1968—page 31.

Townsend, Mrs. Grace—*Imperial Cook Book*—(A Monitor for the American Housewife in the Dining Room and Kitchen)—1894.

Weil, Lorna—*Tour to Note Yule around World*—Allentown Morning Call—Allentown, Penna.—December 12, 1967—page 21.

Wheeler, Holohan, V.—*Boutell's Manual of Heraldry*—Frederick Warne & Co.,—London & New York—1931.

Wyss, Robert L.—*Berner Bauerkeramik*—1966.

Whittemore, Edwin C.—*A Horn Book Cookie Board*—Spinning Wheel—December, 1968—page 37.